£1.50

5/19

GO QUIET INTO THE FRAGRANT NIGHT

. . . .

A BLACK COUNTRY LOVE STORY

BY BILL HIPKISS

COMPILED BY LAURENCE HIPKISS

Dedicated

To Ivy & Bill

I would like to thank Bill's sister Nancy and Ivy's sister and brother Iris and Bill for their kind assistance during the research stage of this book. Thanks also to Anthony Lewis of Great Barr Past and Present and Peter Allen, Chair - Barr & Aston Local History Society for their time and for the historic detail they provided concerning Hamstead Colliery.

I would also like to express a special thank you to Kirsty Greaves of Anthony Phillips and Davis Print and Design for her creative expertise and guidance which helped this dream become a reality.

Published by:
Roosterspake
97 Wendover Road,
Rowley Regis,
West Midlands,
B65 8LQ

email: lozz@blackcountrypodcasting.com
billy.dakin@hotmail.co.uk

Design & Printed by:
Anthony Phillips & Davis
24 Broad Street,
Langley, Oldbury,
West Midlands,
B69 4SF

ISBN: 978-0-9564225-07

Contents

I have chosen the photographs that illustrate this book from my own family album.

All poetry by Bill Hipkiss

Foreword

I read Bill's work many years before I knew he was Lozz's dad. His stories from Langley and Roundabout and poetry in Musings and Meanderings filled my head with great memories of growing up in the area. I would laugh aloud at some of his acute recollections or be stunned by the beauty of a line from one of his many poems. I read Bill as I did other gifted writers and was engulfed in the colour they brought to life from just a word or a line or if writing about experiences how they could take you into this imagery that was tangible. I tell people I began to write in dialect because I felt I needed to make that journey but maybe it was because I could never see myself being able to harness the craft that Bill had over how he wove his words together so brilliantly.

Fate brought Lozz and myself back together after many years and I am honoured to be associated with a man who is not only incredibly gifted in his own right but is a rare human being who I could not have survived without the last few years. Our first meeting was as if we were still kids playing in the same football team and when he told me some of his childhood it was then I made the connection with Bill his father. Unfortunately Bill passed away not long after we got back together and by then I had been humbled when Lozz asked me to put words to the beautiful melodies he had created over the years. The sadness is it wasn't until Bill had passed that Lozz told me of the mountains of work his dad had produced and that he would bring back with him from his dad's house. Even at that early stage we spoke of the need to 'find a place' for it in terms of it being accessible to the public. There was so much and the subject matter immense. Stories, technical pieces, poems a whole host of material and as we were ourselves getting more involved with playing, recording organising festivals and clubs it seemed to drift into the background and get forgotten. I began to read some of Bills work around the folk clubs when I had a 'spot' and it was quite obvious that it would be well received but no matter how many times the subject cropped up there was always something prevented us actually starting anything.

Recently we were sitting in Lozz's living room talking instead of working, as we usually do and he showed me a couple of poems. Very short but beautifully written. I asked what they were. He explained after his mother passed his dad would write a poem for her on every important day each year, birthdays, and so on. These spanned the years till his own death and it was such a personal account of this one mans deep love for his lady. We sat for a minute both looking at the pieces and almost as one said. "This is it. This is the time." I'm so glad we didn't brush them to the back ground as we have done so many times in the past. Some people may say they are too personal but writers cannot be precious about their work. In my view if they are not read or heard then they should be destroyed. Words and voice are there to communicate. They may bring a tear, a laugh, a deep thought but whatever happens they will find some kind of emotion within the reader or listener. This set of poems is without doubt the work of a man whose emotions have been laid bare. They are drowned in warmth and a deep understanding of life and death. I am proud for Lozz, I am proud for his family. I am deeply humbled and honoured to have played a small part in this project. I hope we are able to 'hear these words 'live' and also work together to bring some of Bill's words into our own live sets. This is a glorious , simple, honest, human set of poems and they will mean so much to anyone who sits quietly and lets their emotions take over. To Bill I wish I would have known you. To Ivy, he truly loved you and to Lozz be so proud mucka.

Billy SpakeMon

Bill Aged 17 (1936)

A Stir Of Embers

The coals will burst

with fiery store;

more full of life

than was before.

Introduction

Amongst his many skills and attributes, my father, Bill Hipkiss was an incredibly imaginative writer of both prose and poetry. He had a great love for the written word which I remember him trying to explain to me on several occasions. In fact anyone that knew my dad will probably remember him trying to explain something or other to them, and it would usually be in detail and at great length. He was just that kind of man; he knew things and he was happy to share his knowledge. Actually, I think most Black Country streets probably had a character like my dad in them. If someone needed to know something they would be told to go n' ask Bill Hipkiss he'll know", and of course he usually did. In those dark pre-search engine days before we had computers and the internet to provide all the answers, it was people like my dad that would help a neighbours children with their homework or maybe give advice to a pensioner about filling in a form. Whatever it was he could usually be relied upon to help. Sadly he died just after his 87th birthday in the early hours of the 31st of December 2006. Shortly after his death I promised Martin and Sandra, my brother and sister, that I would chronicle his written work and look into getting it published on a very small scale. This would serve as a memento to be distributed amongst a select group of family and friends. However when I started to read through the material, especially the poetry, I soon realised that it deserved a much wider readership and so I decided to put it into the public domain.

This book is in three parts, but the poetry has just one central theme; the love my father had for his wife, my mother Ivy May. Every poem is a declaration of a deep and everlasting love. What makes this such a thought-provoking collection of writing is that we only ever read one side of this beautiful story. Ivy never has her say, she remains silent and we can only wonder at what her response might have been to this wonderful poetry.

The first part of the book, Yesterday, contains poetry that I feel is relevant to the story. The second part contains birthday and anniversary verse written by Bill and dedicated to Ivy with the intention of adding a personal touch to their shared special days. Whilst I have presented only a small selection of birthday poems, the anniversary verse starts with "Twenty-Three" and continues until "Forty-Ninth" which celebrates their final anniversary together before my mother lost her long and courageous battle with cancer on March the 6th 1991.

MERCER TRANSPORT

T. MERCER LTD.
8
LANGLEY GREEN RD
LANGLEY
N' BIRMINGHAM

PDH 79

The third part of the book is in my view quite overwhelming in its content. After my mothers death my father continued to write verse dedicated to her but which now revealed the heartache that he felt at her loss. Without fail and every year for the rest of his life he wrote short love poems to mark each anniversary that they had once shared during the course of a year. These dates were; their wedding anniversary on the 20th of September, mom's birthday on the 15th of October and his own birthday on the 14th of December (he combined this with Christmas). He added to these dates the 6th of March to mark the occasion of my mothers passing.

The poems were mounted onto a small wooden plaque which he had made himself. He placed the plaque amongst the flowers at my mother's graveside four times a year from 1991 until his own death in 2006. In fact the final poem had been put into place only a few days before he died on New Years Eve 2006.

The following is a very brief introduction to my parents, Bill and Ivy Hipkiss. It is not intended to be a comprehensive biography but more of a brief personal history of the central characters in this story and the events that shaped their lives leading up to their marriage in 1941.

Bill

My father was born on the 14th of December 1919 in his mother's family home at number 12 Titford Road in Langley. That house is now long demolished but a modern house stands in its place. His mother's family, the Edgley's lived in number 12 Titford Road and his father's family the Hipkiss's lived across the road at number 43. Christened James William by his parents Jim and Mary Ellen he took his shortened second name of Will as his preferred title but everyone called him Bill. His mother, who was known to all as Nellie, died just before his sixth birthday in August 1925. Her death was as the result of an illegal medical procedure, commonly known in those days as a backstreet abortion. Bill and his younger sister Nancy, just two and a half years old at that time remained at number 12 with their father, their maternal grandparents and their mother's brother and sister Alec and Zillah. Shortly after Nellie's death, Zillah actually gave up her job to look after the children.

My son Christoph
with his Grandad (199

In 1928 my grandfather got re-married to a woman that would bring real sadness and despair into my father's life. Her name was Lillian Gething and she seemed to be the very antithesis of his mother, she was different in every way. Nellie was a kind sweet natured woman that was loved by everyone she met, but 'momma Lil' as she was to become known, was a brash and ebullient woman who was subject to great fits of rage and temper. The children were both frightened by this new woman in their father's life. Bill later recalled that when he was taken to meet Lil's family in West Bromwich, he was stood in the middle of a small room which was full of strangers and one of the old men in the room, possibly Lil's father, confronted him. The man shouted "open yer gob let's see if yer belly's full". The old man may well have been trying to be friendly but Bill was struck dumb, he had never come across such behaviour before and simply didn't know how to react.

Once they had married, Jim and Lil moved into 43 Titford Road to live with Jim's family, and of course Bill and Nancy had to move in with them. For the children, moving out of number 12 proved to be a painful and difficult separation because by this time they had settled down and were quite happy living in nanny Edgley's house. They were especially happy living with Zillah who was similar in nature to their mother and who had cared for them both with great affection.

Lil on the other hand was not at all good with children and shortly after she had married and taken up her role as stepmother, a near disaster in their home caused a split in the family. Unattended one morning, Bill who was still only nine or ten years old was trying to get himself ready for school and he had put a damp towel onto a rail in front of the fire to dry. Luckily Zillah, who was in the habit of looking in to see that all was well, came across just in time to stop the towel catching fire, which could have burnt the house down, taking Bill and Nancy with it. This caused a great deal of family trouble and Nancy who was already unhappy living with Lil was taken over the road to live with Zillah and her new husband Walter Picken. In time Zillah and Walter arranged to adopt Nancy and she became Nancy Picken. I'm not sure why only one of the children was adopted, it may have been on grounds of age. Nancy was still a very young child and as Lil needed to work such long hours, it may have been decided that adoption was the best solution for everyone. Whatever the reason it did not affect my father's great love and affection for Zillah which continued until her death in 1969.

Ivy, May & Ir

Although Bill's relationship with Lil would scar him for the remainder of his life, in fairness, he always gave credit to his step-mother for being hard working, resourceful and determined. She was a tough woman who held down a hard physical job, that of a metal polisher, and she never shirked her responsibility to bring home a much needed wage.

Despite these problems Bill led a fairly active life which included becoming a choirboy at both Holy Trinity and St Michael's churches in Langley, something that he enjoyed very much. Then of course there were social clubs and concerts in the locality. He also arranged to do extra schoolwork and he studied most evenings after school so that he might earn a place at the County High School in Moat Road. However on the Saturday morning that he was due to sit the entrance examination at Rood End School, Lil flew into one of her rages. An argument followed which ended in Lil telling him that even if he passed the exam he would not be going to the Grammar School. He later wrote that he had walked to Rood End School in tears and when he sat the examination tears were falling onto the paper as he was writing. The outcome of that was inevitable, a few years of secondary education at St Michael's school in Causeway Green Road, Langley. He was fourteen years old when he left school at Christmas 1933 having completed his formal education. Almost straightaway he got himself a position as a lather boy for local barber Archie Connop and he enjoyed this for a while until he decided to move into engineering, his second job was at MCL in Causeway Green, Langley where they made screws and the like. Bill then felt a calling for the sweet trade so he took up a job as a trainee sugar boiler at Parkes's Classical Confectioners in Crosswells Road Langley but he soon tired of that so he moved on to become a delivery boy for local butcher John A. Bates.

It was during this last job that he met Jack Judge the writer of the lyrics to the famous First World War time song 'It's a Long, Long Way to Tipperary'. Dad recalls Judge scribbling verse onto the back of cigarette packets and then discarding them. He told me how he had wished that he had been sensible enough to keep these scraps of card. All of these jobs came and went in the first six months after he had left school.

It was about then in the mid1930's that the family moved to a more modern council house in Hayes Road, Smethwick. Dad had managed to secure yet another job working for Bob Edis at his garage in a yard situated adjacent to the Oldbury side of Oldbury Cemetery in Rood End Road. It was whilst working there that he became acquainted and in fact smitten (his words) with a young girl, Ivy May Mercer the daughter of a local haulage contractor Tom Mercer. Tom kept his lorries parked in the same yard in Rood End and Ivy would occasionally come into the yard with either her father or one of his drivers. Of course she would probably have treated Bill with some disdain after all she was the daughter of a reasonably successful businessman and Bill was just a humble mechanic. This playful character trait would epitomise their relationship in later years.

It was also at around this time and after one too many arguments with momma Lil that Bill packed his bags and left home. He was now fifteen or sixteen years old and didn't have to be ordered around by this bully of a woman. He walked to Titford Road and asked Zillah if he could lodge with her for a while. She agreed and Bill moved back to number 12 Titford Road where he lived very happily with Aunt Zillah, Uncle Walter, Uncle Alec, Nanny Edgley and his sister Nancy. This arrangement continued until Bill volunteered for duty at the outbreak of the Second World War in 1939.

Ivy

My mother was born on the 15th of October 1921 to Thomas Henry and Ethel May Mercer (nee Finch). She was christened Ivy May Mercer and was the eldest of four children, the others being Ken (Kenneth Gordon), Iris and Bill (Thomas William).

Tom Mercer's family came from Oldbury and he was a First World War veteran that had served in the Worcestershire Regiment in the trenches of northern France where he had been badly wounded and gassed. Soon after the war he lost both his father and a brother to flu in the great pandemic of 1918/19.

May Mercer, as she preferred to be known, came from West Bromwich and many of the men in her family, the Finches, were miners at The Hamstead Colliery. Sadly, May's older brother Albert was killed in the mine on July 18th 1911 at 7.50 pm when the roof collapsed on top of him. He was crushed by ten feet of coal and it took five hours to extricate his body. He was thirty six years old.

njoying the view Ivy?

The Mercers lived in various locations which included St Pauls Road in Smethwick, Portway Hill in Oldbury, Langley Green Road in Langley and lastly Moat Road in Oldbury. The home that is most relevant to this story is the rented yard and accommodation they lived in at 23 Langley Green Road. Known throughout the Mercer family as simply '23'.it was whilst Ivy was living at this address that my parents' relationship blossomed.

The reason the Mercers moved to 23 was because Tom needed to expand his business and in every way a move to 23 made sense. He needed his own yard with garages and an office and at 23 he had all of these things. Tom Mercer earned most of his income from the transport and supply of coal. This was brought into the area by rail and delivered to the sidings at Oldbury Station. Tom's drivers loaded their lorries by hand and then delivered it throughout the region to factories and manufacturers such as Tube Products, Danks's and Metal Closures. He eventually owned and operated four lorries from the yard at 23 and employed a number of drivers including Frank Jones (Foreman) and brothers Harry and Stuart Foster. Not only was Tom successful but he was also a very kind man. Family members still recall that to celebrate the end of hostilities after the Second World War he arranged for two of his lorries to be decked out with seating and he invited as many locals that could get on board to join him and his family on a day trip to the Clee Hills. In the days of fuel rationing just after the war, this was an incredibly generous thing to do.

Obviously, because her family now lived in Langley, Ivy was regularly seen in the town. Dad's sister Nancy told me that she already knew who Ivy was before she was connected to my dad in any way. I think that it's probable that Ivy and Bill were on nodding terms at the very least before their first romantic liaison which I am informed took place at the newly opened Langley Baths, on a Sunday morning in 1937. The baths would have been used for swimming during the summer but for dancing during the winter months and I believe Bill's poem "Sweet and Low Played the Band" was inspired by one such occasion at Langley Baths.

A four year courtship followed only to be interrupted by the outbreak of war in 1939. They were married at St Michael's church, Langley on the 20th of September 1941 and a lavish reception was held at the Kings Highway.

Ivy seems to have been happy and content throughout most of her childhood and it's fairly clear that she had a much happier early life than Bill. Because of this lack of early detail I have decided to add some anecdotal information to help to create an impression of the character and personality of the woman for whom my father wrote the wonderful verse contained within this book.

The first short story portrays Ivy as a warm but slightly dizzy character. When I was told that I had passed my 11 plus exam in around 1964 I remember Mom being very proud. However, not to be outdone, she told me that she would have easily passed her 11 plus (or equivalent) if only she hadn't fallen off her chair during the test and been asked to leave the room. That sort of story was typical of my mom.

My second story is far more serious and shows great courage and strength of character. In her early sixties Ivy was diagnosed with cancer of the oesophagus for which there was no cure. However, if she agreed to have her oesophagus removed which would also include the removal of her vocal chords she would have a reasonable chance of leading a fairly normal life. She agreed to the operation and after some time in hospital she had recovered sufficiently to be allowed home. It was then that the reality of facing the world without a voice had to be dealt with. This outgoing, gregarious and popular woman that loved to chat suddenly had to learn to communicate without speech. I remember that after the operation some people would never be able to relax in her company ever again and others would talk around her as if she were not in the room at all. Some even talked louder to her as if she were hard of hearing or disabled in some other way. The pain and frustration of all this must have been immense but she carried it bravely. Eventually and with the help and support of the Sandwell Hospital Speech Therapy Unit, she was given a vibro-voice, a small buzzing vibrator that when held against the throat would provide sound for words that were mouthed. She could now talk again, albeit with an electronic voice that sounded unnatural and which was actually quite loud. Of course Ivy who was a proud woman was very aware of this and she would instantly pick up on people staring at her in public. It took time but she got used to using the machine and I will never forget the first time that she used it to phone me at my office. I was so shocked and pleased, that it was I that could not speak for a while.

After that, she soon got back into the familiar routine of shopping, hairdressers and family visits. She even made a return to her favourite night out with her friends at the Rex Bingo hall in Blackheath, which stood on the site that Sainsbury's now occupies. Bingo was all the rage in the 1980's and Ivy (but definitely not Bill) was an avid participant.

Throughout all of this pain and suffering Ivy was supported by family members and friends but it was Bill that really helped her through it. He was her rock and he never left her side during her long illness. When the cancer returned in the late 1980's, again he was her constant companion and carer.

Ivy slipped away silently in Bill's arms on the 6th of March 1991 at our family home in Kenelm Road, Oldbury she was 69 years old. This was the house that they had lived in for over forty-five years and in which they had raised their family. I was born in the front room of that house on January 23rd 1953.

In the years that followed Bill became actively involved with local history groups and was even asked to judge a poetry competition for pupils at Langley High School, the modern name of the very school he had dreamed of attending when he was a boy.

As I mentioned earlier Bill died of a heart attack on the 31st of December 2006 at Sandwell Hospital in West Bromwich, he was 87.

Laurence Hipkiss

My brother & sister Martin & Sandra

Yesterday...

Yesterday

And shall we not in hours to come
think yesterday was young;
and rue we whittled, scorned and spurned,
and squandered time we had.

With reckless haste we hailed the years
and welcomed gross maturity.
Undue the glee - we bade farewell
to innocence.

With what conceits we now compound
vain thoughts beset us then!

Bill Hipkiss

Sweet And Low Played the Band

All those portraits and plaques, civic graces and airs -
so impressive, but so was the dancing upstairs,
where we gingerly revelled in days that are spent;
I remembered, and wondered where all that time went.
As I stirred dying embers, rose ghost-wise the dance
that gave rise to an early, impromptu romance. . . .

I can still feel the pulse of that music above,
my young heart was in bloom - I was all but in love;
so I posed, and she simpered and fingered her tress,
and I toyed with my tie - and I ogled, no less.
I was all of a fluster but made my advance,
with a diffident gesture I asked her to dance;
though I mumbled and bumbled she knew what I meant,
just a flick of a smile and she gave her assent.
In a flutter of heart-beats I took to the floor,
where we quick-stepped and waltzed as I'd never before;
with a splash of panache a slow fox-trot or two,
and we tangoed with steps that were patently new -
and the more my success at avoiding her toes,
so the smile lit her face and my confidence rose.

Sweet and low played the band as we skipped to the park,
where a honey-bright moon was beguiling the dark.
I can still see the moon-beams cascade through her hair,
and the eyes all a-glint, comprehending my prayer;
feel that thin, icy tremor uprooting my spine
as her painstaken lips gave an answer like wine.
Loud and strong beat my heart in tattoos of delight,
as the last of my qualms slid away to the night;
round and round in my head swam refrains of the day,
in wild rhythm my lips consummated each lay.
Sleepy beds came alive with the hum of guitars,
and the pool seemed to dance with the glister of stars.

All the stately old trees played the murmuring breeze -
in the reaches of madness such moments as these!
Yet as moon-shadows lengthened, caressing the grass,
so the portals of paradise shattered like glass;
much in hope had I ventured, bemused by delight,
but she pointed and murmured, "I live there, goodnight!"

And the quirky old moon gave a snigger of glee -
but I heard the Paul Jones, it was playing for me. . . .
Face about went the promenade till the band stopped,
then my heart slipped a beat and my eyes fairly popped;
my new partner was gorgeous, I soared like a lark,
and I waltzed her back homeward - but not through the park!

Now as old autumn bites, chills, and rivels the bones,
from afar comes the echo of strident Paul Jones;
then the sap's on the upturn, it's spring-time once more -
and I'm there wi' me boots blacked, back there on the floor.
And if only that moon would shine bright - oh, so bright
through some fair maiden tresses, that heaven-borne night;
I would pray to the skies for some wise, guiding light,
for to stay that fine filly from rearing with fright.

Ivy & Bill

September Song

Sigh, September, twilit sighs -
shed not tears; they must fall
for whom September comes through veils;
they are an ever far-off dream -
once unfolded in the sun.
They loved once, September;
they loved your mist-eyed dawns,
and soft-sprung days; and gentle rain
that held no threat to disconcert
down lover's lane.
Bide, September, bide awhile -
though leaves are scuffed,
and birds flown that summer's known -
and nights grow long, and winter's bite
is in the bones.
Sing, September, songs for me
you erstwhile sang - I'll have a beating,
captive heart, and know again
the burning flame; I'll sigh no more,
September song.
And love me now; I stood
enraptured once - you loved me then.
I soft inhaled your dreamy nights,
and breezy days and would the more September.

Madge Hipkiss, Gwen Nock, Bill Mercer (Front), Bill & Ivy Hipkiss, Tom Mercer, Nancy Picken, Iris Mercer

Langley

Langley Village is my love -
it is my Valentine;
It is the place which all above
the rest my love will shine.
And if you ask why this should be -
I tell you it's my home;
it's here I bide, and here I'd stay,
and never need to roam.

Bill's Parents Wedding Photo (August 1919)
Wilf Bath, Nancy Jones, Jim & Nelly Hipkiss (nee Mary Ellen Edg|
Zillah Edgley, Grandad Edgley

Local Weddings

CROWDED CHURCH FOR LANGLEY CEREMONY

St. Michael's Church, Langley, was filled for the wedding of Miss Ivy May Mercer, daughter of Mr. and Mrs. T. H. Mercer, of 23, Langley Green Road, Langley, and Driver James William Hipkiss (R.A.S.C.) son of Mr. J. T. Hipkiss and the late Mrs. Hipkiss, 255, Queen's Road, Warley. The Rev. J. W. Povah conducted the service.

The bride, who was given in marriage by her father, wore a crinoline gown of white net, tulle, taffeta and lace, trimmed with bunches of white lilac. Her headdress was of white gardenias and orange blossom, and she wore white crepe satin shoes, and carried a bouquet of white carnations, gladiolae and stocks.

The bridesmaids were the Misses Nancy Picken (sister of the bridegroom), Gwen Nock (friend of the bride), Iris Mercer (sister of the bride), and Madge Hipkiss (sister of the bridegroom). Their dresses were of white net, tulle and taffeta trimmed with bunches of white lilac and green ribbon and they wore green satin shoes. Their bouquets were similar to that carried by the bride. The older bridesmaids' hats were in Edwardian style, of green velvet trimmed with white net. The younger bridesmaids had Kate Greenaway bonnets of green velvet. The bride was also attended by a page boy, wearing a white satin blouse, green velvet trousers and silver slippers. He carried a bunch of white heather.

The gowns, bouquets and accessories were supplied by Wyne Allen, Oldbury.

Mr. Jack Edgley, of the Coldstream Guards (cousin of the bridegroom) was best man.

A reception was held at the King's Highway Hotel, Quinton, and was attended by about 90 guests.

Many useful presents were received.

Anniversary Verse

This section is in two parts, the first a few poems composed for Ivy
on her birthday and the second, starting with twenty-three, verse
written to mark the occasion of every wedding anniversary.

Dear Iv'

Now that you're not twenty-two,

I can't say I regret,

'Twas nice you being twenty-two,

but yet I cant forget –

that when you first were twenty-two,

then I was twenty-three:

so how could you be be twenty-two

now I am thirty-three.

My love the autumn doth o'er shadow

fine drawn lights of summer high;

and so we mourn for summer lost –

and well we may – and sigh.

O Iv' you're in the plight

of all of us down 'ere

----ty-three you were last night,

----ty-four now morn is here.

O Iv' I don't know what to say,

except to wish you – Happy Birthday.

and though the years may flow and flow

'tis no cause to regret,

for as another year does go

perchance it may beget

more joy for you than that you know;

look on, take heart, and no regret

Ivy, Sandra,
Martin & Myself (front)

Thirty Plus

If golden time was all I had,
and time was only gold,
a nonsense of a verse would weigh
in gold a thousandfold.

And though I bear no frankincense,
or myrrh – or fine, rare spice –
I trust the dredges of my mind
for this day will suffice.

What care the mumblings of a world,
steeped in old Bacchus' way?
my worldly wealth, forever yours –
my heart and soul, today.

. . . .

Fifty Plus

Night, and the pregnant dreams of slumber
gather in the moonbeams' wake;
soon the senseless hours will number
fancies that the wits forsake.

May every dream of every night-fall
gather for this one day's sake –
and may the magic of their moments
savour every breath you take

Nineteen Seventy
Blinkin' Eight

I lick my wounds,
and shoulder glances
through the splintered chinks
of passing blinds –
and see the ghosts
of salad days re-forming there.

Yet onward ever onward,
to the golden crest
of some dark hill –
I speak not of the leaden days,
but silver nights
on crimson wings;
and rueful, rueful as may be,
they all will join
the salad ghosts
in splintered glances
through the passing blinds.

And time is only of the mind,
and mind is only of the will –
so time is what we make it,
nothing more.

Sixty Plus

Another fall of burning gold,
another harvest gathered in;
another summer's song is song,
another year has made its mark –
and left fond traces in the dust.

The winnowing winds through years to come
will smooth your footsteps into mine,
and breathe them into timeless space –
so may the essence of our days in dust entwine.

But now the task be more mundane,
a path to make for both our gain

Twenty Three

I have seen the tall trees
wherein the birds sing;
I have felt the strong wind,
and the pelting rain sting.

The buds in the hedgerow
of brilliant green,
and white-flowering May
just fit for a queen.

I have heard the proud lark
sing its song on the wing;
felt a throb in my breast –
felt alive – in the spring.

These I have known,
and these I would give,
just for the chance
these years to relive.

.   .   .   .   .   .

I think if I remember right
today's the date we took the dive;
as I recall tonight's the night
that we were lucky to survive.

I seem to smell chloride-of-lime,
see ammo-boots, and battle dress;
and – just to make this stanza rhyme –
let's say I looked a bloody mess.

But you – of course – you looked so nice,
and smelled so good, and looked so pure;
I'd say some more, but in a trice,
you'd sense the old, sweet overture.

And now that three-and-twenty years
have rolled away, but not to mind,
I see no need for any tears,
'cos I think life's been pretty kind.

And I hope there will be plenty more,
– not what you think, but that'll do –
whatever fate has got in store,
I hope it will be for us two.

. . . .

For a Score and four

A world within a world is yours, is mine, is ours;
yet 'twould be vain pretence – unworthy of this day,
to portray thus a bed of flowers, and pleasant hours,
unmindful of the rifts and tiffs, and plans astray.

Yet dream within a dream has been, 'tis now, 'twill be;
but as all dreamers, waking, find a world less kind,
so will we sleep, maybe, unto eternity,
and find within that sleep, dreaming, all we wish to find.

Bill & Ivy

Silver

Is the dew drop on the rose at dawn
a surfeit of delight?
Who bids the fragrant blossom fade
into the winter's blight?

And does the nightingale that floods
the recess of the night,
not beg the plea that time shall pause
its endless, boundless flight?

Is it too long that we have spent
as one – or will the night
not come from day? My troth again,
to stay your fears, I plight.

When Summer is Gone

The blooms of the rose-bed,
translucent with dew;
full-bodied and rich
with evening's deep hue –
tell me that summer wears on.

Twenty-six roses ablaze on the bush
tell of a summer that's high;
tell of the bliss of an oft-savoured kiss –
a soft, mellow autumn that's nigh.
And if they be red roses, tell of a love
that's flaming when summer is gone.

The birds in the tree top
sing sweet with the dawn,
sing sweeter at evening
before night has sorn.

Twenty-six songbirds in voice on a limb,
tell of the oboe and flute;
tell of the choir, the aisle and the ring –
a belfry so painfully mute.
And if they be turtle-doves, tell of a love
that's singing when summer is gone.

The summer is parting;
the leaves on the tree
be-golden the skyline
and soon they'll be free –
telling me summer is gone.

Twenty-six summers awash on the log,
tell of the turbulent tides;
tell of the wave that has carried afar –
of twenty-six winters besides.
And if they be true enough, tell of a love
that's summer when summer is gone.

Ivy & Bill

Thought for Today
(26 continued)

O for the pen of the Avon bard!
A fine flutter of words I'd brood;
I'd lyric long into the night,
probe each thought – explore each mood.

A spoor would hide 'neath every mot;
and every comma, point and mark,
would counterpoint my nuances
through every shade from light to dark.

But all these efforts would be vain
if I have not given cause to say:
"Through twenty-six years as your wife,
I hold no real regrets today."

And if this be so – as I would hope –
I give you all my fondest love;
but if by chance I am too vain,
'tis my regret – but yet my love.

For Ivy With Love
(27, '68)

What need we of memories who have in the span
of a moment of loving a lifetime of bliss?
Who have captivated the warmth of the years,
to be lavished unspared in the space of a kiss.

What need we of markers who judge not the time
by the passage of sunsets or season or sign?
But only by partings or pleasant returns,
and by weaving the web with our true-love's design.

Yet I have some fond memories I hope we can share
when the rosy complexion has slid from our days;
and I'll still keep this day till the seas have run dry'
and the warp and the weft gone their own separate ways.

. . . .

1969

Night and the pregnant dreams of slumber
gather in the moonbeams' wake;
soon the senseless hours will number
fancies that the wits forsake.

My every dream of every nightfall
gather for this one day's sake –
and may the magic of their moments
savour every breath you take.

1970

How fleet the span, how sweet the urge,
how pleasant fliers the shaft at Cupid's will.
The days arrive, the days depart,
and all is change – and yet is likeness still.
And now my love this day is ours –
although with dearth much more than riches fill.

. . . .

1971

To Ivy – for Ivy –
a flowery token,
a poor substitution for
what's in my heart;
but I give you this emblem
of words unspoken,
love and affection
words cannot impart.

. . . .

1972, to Ivy With Love

That time is only of the mind,
I have been known, myself, to say;
but I confess to shades of doubt
that this is so today.

Yet I regret not what has been
(except I'd put my wrongs to right),
but I'm afraid I can't repeat
my score upon that certain night.

1973

Tonight the moon is in the trees,
the stars thread through the leaves;
incipient autumn springs the breeze
that flusters through the eaves.

And I am here alone, and true
in my undying way.
I know not what on earth to do
as morning brings the day.

To bear no gifts will be my lot,
I fear you'll take it hard –
but worse, I'm 'fraid I quite forgot
to get a bloomin' card.

. . . .

1974

Standing on its head,
where I put it,
Time waits –
waits awhile
you ponder on
the message of this day.

1975

Swift are the wings of Time
that gather all the sunlit hours
and cast them on the slow, slow stream.

Sweet is the breath of Time
that winnows through the hearts and flowers
and sorts them into one long dream.

. . . .

1976

It's hard to think
what would be now
if all the things
now done and gone
had not been so –
so no regrets
are valid ones.

But easier
to see that now
is bearable,
and easily
could be so worse
that I could not
with honest heart
say that this is
a happy day.

To Ivy – Thirty-plus (1977)

If golden time was all I had,
and time was only gold,
a nonsense of a verse would weigh
in gold a thousand-fold.

Although I bear no frankincense,
or myrrh – or fine, rare spice –
I trust the dredges of my mind
for this day will suffice.

what care the mumblings of a world
steeped in old Bacchus' way?
My worldly wealth, forever yours –
my heart and soul today.

James Hipki
(Bill's Fathe

Thirty-seven (1978)

(To my wife Ivy, to whom
for thirty-seven years I've been wed;
and hope to be till the crack of doom –
I'll be a long time dead.)

So,
September twenty's
here again!

If I should ask,
'What is today?'
You'd think me acting strange,
or playing for a funny line,
or stringing up a word or two,
or else, as is my wont,
just plain forgot.

But seasons that have passed and gone,
golden autumns, winter snows,
each burst of spring that led
us on to all those summer rains:
yet not until this moment dawned
has this quite simple thought
sprung up beneath my brow:
it also marks the summer's close.

I hope this ordinary fact
strikes not a note of morbid thought
within your mind.

And still the seams of seasons sewn
with threads of love a thousand-fold,
lend to the passing folds of time
soft overtones of peace of mind.

1979

The summer's tent is broken –
broke, as though it never was,
except in glimmers of goodbye
across the hues of dying green;
and in the shimmering spectres
flitting fitful through the recent mind.

So long have summers lost their drapes,
their vestment shed with languid ease;
so long our summers all congealed –
set into one sweet, pleasant haze:
so long to we who dare to hold
a candle to old Heim's dark mien.

And I who care will hold a flame
to keep a fire so taken well.

. . . .

1980

I feel a tinge of sorrow
as the summer's passing on;
the only spasm of regret
to mar this day we share –
except, perhaps (a vain, vain dream),
that all had just begun.

1981 (Ruby)

September's sultry skies are measured now,
and while they stay
are but a dream that weeps awhile.

And weeps a deeper weeping by and by –
as summer's day
is but a breath that scarcely was.

And soon a maiden autumn sings of fire
that sweeps away
the eventide of all that's done.

September's mellow moon will tell you all
that I should say –
and say it soft and warm and true.

(And say that magic moments need not all
be of 'Milk Tray' –
but Black perhaps . . . if rather small.)

1982

And not one moment less
than all the years that we have shared
would be an happy thought.

And not one eon more
than all the moments we have stored
would be for me too much.

And not one golden day or shower of rain,
one hour of play or wreath of pain
a surplus to my wants.

1983

Altar-wise by moonlight,
flitter-mouse twittering;
softly the night owl
swoops slyly blinking;
fond retrospection
eternally sighing . . .

The shepherd is poised,
the flock congregating;
appropriate melodies
rafter-wards winging;
all else attendant –
incipient mating.

The groom is resplendent,
boots and brass gleaming;
distaff and spear
their opposites spying –
hope that the bride's not
as they are, expecting.

She was, and she got it,
but far from complaining,
she made every incident
most entertaining –
I'm sick as a goose
that I'm only remembering.

1984

Sincerely yours to jog the mind
to raise some tender thoughts of yore;
and think on days that slowly wind
to take away – and yet give more.

. . . .

1895

Summer slowly slips away,
and autumn ambles into view;
thank you for another year
of care and love with you.

. . . .

1986

And sometimes when what needs is done,
and shall be made is made;
when all the winning has been won,
all songs are sung, games played –
the laggard fingers creep the mocking face.

Yet there are days seem all so near –
some yesterdays or so.
The times I found so very dear,
why were they soon to go?
As disappear they did at such a pace.

1987

Oh, goodness, dear Ivy. Oh, what shall I do!

My licence is up for my being with you.

It's not that I don't want to go on you see,

It's just that I won't pass my next M.O.T..

As birds choose their mates round the old cherry tree,

oh, goodness, dear Ivy, I wish it was me.

The blooms that emblazoned and livened the green,

now dead-headed memories of all that has been.

. . . .

1988

Once more the season closes

wild with sweet, September rain.

Once more the leaves begin to shed,

once more I say again –

though all the years may come and go

I hope to make you see,

a special place within my heart

this one day holds for me.

May Mercer (Ivy's Mother)

Eight-and-Forty – Gee-Whiz!

The golden years have run amok
and tumbled madly – sadly gone;
but here, today, can pause awhile
and take a stock of all the won,
the lost, the 'might-have-beens' –
and in the end just soldier on.

. . . .

Forty-Ninth

There came this lilting, old-time lover's lay,
encapsulating all I thought I new
that I could want – and did, I'm glad to say –
when life was young and love was something new.

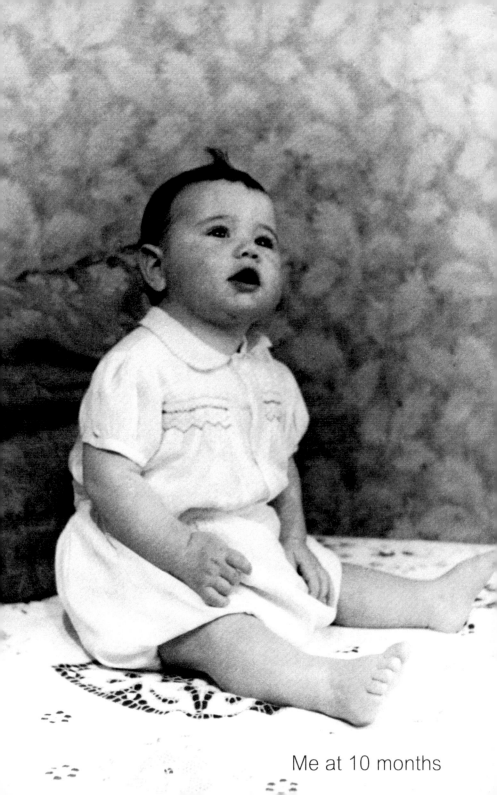
Me at 10 months

In Sad Conclusion

Obviously during my research for this book I have had to read through a huge amount of dads writing. One of the difficulties I have had is trying to determine which variant of each poem Bill considered to be the finished version. He would write and re-write several times before the final piece emerged. Sometimes the final version would only differ in the use of a comma or a semi-colon. He would often ponder such things for some time before making a decision.

Amongst the paperwork and material I had to read through I found the following lines written by Bill himself concerning the work contained in second part of this book.

...sadly, she (Ivy) passed away on Wednesday, March 6th, 1991, at about 2-30 p.m. The only consolation I have is that she died at home and in my arms; and she had suffered terrible misery and anguish for almost ten years, and especially during the last six months

She was a lovely woman, very popular, and a first-class, loving wife to me;

and a good and loving mother and grandmother.

I miss her so much.

In the Book of Memory at Powke Lane cemetery I had these lines written:

For that which only pain I find

I grant not sorrow's touch:

but grieve in pain for one so loved

now time is thief of such.

The following lines are to commemorate not only the celebration of our lives together, but also, in addition, Christmas, and especially March 6th. At these times a little notice is placed among the flowers for a while.

Bill Hipkiss

Again in Bill's own words written just a few moths after he had lost Ivy,

One Sunday I was tending Ivy's grave when I noticed a little girl of about four or five years of age picking daisies from the grassy area round each plot. When I came home I was mowing the lawn, and the inevitable daisies, when the memory of that little girl came to me – the innocence of a child, apparently unaware of the significance of the place. Words came, I worked them over in my head as I mowed, wrote them out, and with one or two minor changes since, this is what they came to:

To a Little Girl in Powke Lane Cemetery

She was making a chain of daisies;

as free as the wind in her tan-brown hair,

she was bright as a buttercup, sweet as a rose,

plucking the chosen from here and from there.

She trod in the sun around all that remains

of she once made daisy-chains – gone!

Gone like those daisies so woven with care

when all of their blooming has done.

Weave on then my pretty one, pay you no heed

the while you are able – care not what I say,

but she that I love so lies under this stone;

a-weaving she went in her lovely, bright day:

yet more than sweet daisies, she wove a deep spell

that tangled my heart-strings did my Ivy May.

Bill Hipkiss, Summer 1991

Ivy aged 10

Valediction

Winnowing through the vernal grasses,
softly so, your last goodbye;
spoken not, but in the soughing
through the trees an answering sigh:
weeping not, but in the weeping
of the soft, spring rain – and I.

You, so part of every spring-time –
in the spring-time now are gone;
only memory's mellow caverns
keep your footsteps echoing on:
in the garden of my love will bloom
a deep-red rose – anon.

. . . .

Swift are the wings of Time
that gather all the sunlit hours
and cast them on the slow, slow stream.

Sweet is the breath of Time
that winnows through the hearts and flowers
and moulds them into one long dream.

. . . .

You leave me now and leave a void
that neither toil nor pleasure fill;
and yet in all I think and do
I find you there beside me still.

Go quiet into the fragrant night,
at rest from misery and pain;
at ease with those you loved before,
till I be with you once again.

Ivy, 20th \September, 1991 (Golden Wedding Day).
Immortal time stands 'twixt us now
who once shared blossoms in the spring;
and nigh on fifty years a vow,
a home, a life, a love, a ring –
but golden years were one and all
though snagged and snarled along the way –
but pray you know I loved you then,
and love you still my Ivy, May.

. . . .

15th October, 1991
Fond remembrance, Iv'.
Treasured thoughts
of happier days
we shared.

. . . .

Christmas 1991
Filled with sadness, filled with grief,
the heart you filled beyond belief
with pleasure in its every guise –
and with a love that never dies.
This token but the merest trace
of loss that nothing can replace.

For Ivy, March 6th, 1992

This year gone by has stretched to break
with melancholy and regret;
perverse though fate tore us apart,
in essence you are with me yet.

This lonely hand of mine still feels
your fingers urging, grasping tight –
more eloquent than words could tell.
Sleep quiet in the fragrant night.

. . . .

Remembering – September-twenty, '41 (Sept 92)

Such happiness was mine that day
no ransom for a king could buy;
each lonely night and aimless day
begs answer to a well-worn, 'Why?'
Haply the answer lies with in some scheme –
Haply to live that day again, my dream.

. . . .

Ivy, 15th October, '92

Hither at the whim of chance,
thither on unbridled fate;
blooming for me in golden hours
your fragrance lingers on, and on.

Bill & Ivy's Wedding September 20th 1941

Ivy, Christmas, 1992

If I am dreaming let me wake!
If I'm awake, set me to dream
of times we loved – now sadly gone.

Happier days I can't forget,
and mark their loss with deep regret.

. . . .

Ivy, 6th March, 1993

You are not here. but where I am
the day and whole night through;
no anguish sighs, no memory stirs
but sighs and stirs for you.

. . . .

Ivy, In Remembrance of
20th September, 1941

Time sweeps on, this time we borrow;
time, they say, bears all away.
Change my every joy to sorrow –
And leave me only this, our day.

. . . .

Ivy, October 15th, 1993 – Birthday Thoughts

Unspoken witness marks my love
on this day year by year;
yesterday is all I have
to feel your presence near.

Another Christmas, Iv' (93)
I'm missing you always –
as always I will.
No pleasure this season
This longing will still

. . . .

Ivy, March 6th, 1994
How fast they flew , the years;
How sad to end in tears:
How happy to have known
and shared those days now flown.

. . . .

20th September, 1994
Still is time for they that dream –
dream of what they would again.
Dream of what they would redeem –
haply, still a moments pain.

. . . .

October 15th, 1994
Begat, beloved, we stay awhile –
to laugh, to cry, to play awhile;
soft dreams we dream, and love awhile:
but sadly, sadly, just a while.

Ivy, Christmas, '94

A token of the evergreen;
as memories I hold
of all the pleasant times we shared –
of love that grew not cold.

. . . .

Ivy, March 6th, 1995

In dreams I see the smile you smiled for me,
and hear fond words come whispering to my ear;
my waking hours would pass in pleasant ways
if not bereft of all I hold most dear.

. . . .

Ivy, September 20th, '95

Wert not for this,
this golden day
would be illumed
in Love's old way:
wert not for this.

Mary Ellen & Zillah

Anniversary Thoughts –

And time, they say, bears all away;
and time it is a precious thing;
but time, that ends our little day,
leaves memories that each hour may bring.

And time, 'tis true, bears all away
upon some airy, silver stream;
but echoes of this peerless day
recur like some revolving theme.

And time it is a precious thing;
but dearer for fond memories' spring.

. . . .

Ivy, October 15th, 1995

Time is ruthless, seldom kind;
time is space within the mind.
Time is thief – and when it steals,
Time burrs over, never heals.

. . . .

Ivy, Christmas, 1995

This season of good-will and cheer
brings sadness in its wake;
for those we love no longer here –
for whom the senses ache.
Fond recollections come so dear,
But scant amends they make.

March 6th, 1996

The soft approach of one more spring –
what consolation can it bring?
What empty hours can sunshine fill –
what wakening life an anguish still?
In twilit hours I see your smile,
and wrest a little peace awhile.

. . . .

Fifty-fifth, 20th September, '96

It's not so light, the heart today,
nor full of days ahead;
sad though it is, all must away,
and love's last words be said –
and nought but echoes fondly stay.

. . . .

Ivy, October 15th, 1996

A memory of the happier days
we shared and loved in all its ways;
and dreamed no parting ever thus –
a vain, vain hope for such as us.
But, haply, in some other sphere
we'll love again as we loved here.

. . . .

For Ivy, Christmas 1996

Though love can bridge this
awesome chasm,
no heart can span the
yawning void
this season highlights
all too sadly.

Ivy, March 6, 1997

Time will not wipe away the tears,
nor will one moment live again;
my time is not in measured years
but flick'ring shadows on the pane.

. . . .

Ivy, September 20, 1997

Summer's end, and month of rain,
autumn's drift to winter's bane;
but yet my song is not in vain –
September's lilt to love's refrain
a dream to live and live again.

. . . .

Birthday Memories, Iv',
15th October, 1997

You came, you went, you made your mark
Upon the road we all must rove;
and as I wend my own long walk
you set my feet in ways of love.

. . . .

Ivy, Christmas, 1997

In recollection days fly back
so quickly, O so fast.
In retrospection they moved on
so quickly, O too fast.

Ivy 20th September 1941

Ivy, March 6th, 1998

Just once again to hear you call;
to hear your welcome footsteps fall;
to see the imp within your smile –
once more to hold you for a while.
Just once again, not let you go –
you did, it seems so long ago!

. . . .

Sept. 20, Fifty-seven Years (1998)

Long-while, September was all song,
And flick'ring images of light;
September's song of late is mute,
the dreams have faded to the night.

. . . .

Ivy, Birthday October 15, '98

Just a marker of memory
you left behind,
and the vacant space so hard
to fill, I find.

. . . .

Ivy, Christmas 1998

So far but yet so near;
though far but still so dear.

March 6th, 99
No time for tears that cannot heal
or sighs that cannot mend;
the chasm lies too deep for pain,
nor can assuagement tend.

. . . .

September 20th, 1999
As summer ends
and autumn's on the brink
I think of that far summer's
end with all to have and hold.

. . . .

October 15th, '99
Though all that comes in joy
must sadly, sadly, go –
the knowing of such going
bids less the lonely tears.

. . . .

Xmas, '99
Knowing the pleasures
that once were shared,
forlorn the tiresome joy
but in vain, lonesome thoughts.

March 6th, 2000

You came unknown –
to cast a light,
to make a lifelong mark.
Unbidden, you went –
but known, you left
so deep such pools of gloom.

. . . .

September 20th, 2000

Once more the pleasure
crowds the mind –
but vainly now,
but welcome more.

. . . .

October 15th, 2000

Am I so glad that once
we shared a life!
Am I so sad no more
to hold your hand!
And now, bereft, and left
with but a dream or two!

. . . .

Ivy, Christmas, 2000

Nothing's like Christmas
to glisten with thought
of more happy days spent –
but so patiently wrought;
now – sweet memories of you
and the times that we knew.

Ivy, March 6th, 2001

In Time's busy garden
sweet roses must fade;
but fair redolence hangs
in one rose's fair shade:
oh, for once more to see
one just so rare to me.

Ivy, on our Sixtieth, 20th September, 2001

We who were joined
those years ago,
I tell myself in the violet,
evening hours –
we are not, or ever will be,
apart.

. . . .

Ivy, October 15th, 2001

You and I a symbol made
as day drew to a close;
a bond, a hope, a life,
upon a time as this.

. . . .

Ivy, Christmas, 2001

Not long enough, the days we shared –
in love and strife, in smiles and tears.
Our best was done, we made the most –
immortal dreams, but mortal fears.

Ivy, 6th March, 2002

Let me soar above the sadness,
all the pain that fills my heart,
and recollect the hours of gladness –
ended we had to part.

. . . .

Ivy, 20th September, 2002

I stood awhile and gazed and gazed;
my thoughts were set on backward days:

'Whereof the sun that once beguiled?
My heart, brimful of song,
bethought itself forever young.'

. . . .

October 15, 2002

Not as in the days we knew –
this is not a happy day:
random thoughts yet play their part
in just, for me, one special way.

. . . .

Christmas 2002

A time for loving and to live,
A time to take, and time to give;
for laughing, singing – and to weep:
and to sow – perchance to reap
and store within the mind's long keep.

ancy Garratt (nee Picken) - Bill's Sister

March 6th, 2003

Some memories fade along the way,
with every passing year;
but you are with me every day,
and every moment dear.
Though full of sadness and regret,
Never, never to forget.

. . . .

September 20, 2003

Soft the touch of summer thought
each soft September day;
as soft the thought of times we shared,
and thought were there to stay.

. . . .

October 15, 2003

Now, as soft October leaves
fall and flitter to the ground,
my thoughts abound
with love that once we found.

. . . .

Ivy, Christmas, 2003

So sad that I but tokens bring,
So sad, but in their wake
are tokens of a heart that's filled
with undiminished ache.

March 6th, 2004

The wise one shakes his knowing head,
"All paths converge where all must tread,
and all betwixt is but a dream,
the dream flows on, as does a stream:
and dreamers dream into the night,
the all-pervading, fragrant night."

. . . .

Ivy, 20th September, '04

Days come and go along their way,
some choose but to remain;
but one stays close within my thoughts
as one to live again.
Ivy, thoughts on your birthday

. . . .

15th October, 2004

Birthday thoughts, pride of place,
others, more mundane, are lost;
birthday thoughts, a pair of gloves,
a shaken head, a glad riposte –
your choice, my gain,
to unknown someone's cost.

. . . .

Ivy, Xmas, 2004

How can you hear my heart,
it won't speak above its sighs?
This is the time above all else
When thoughts, so fond, of you arise.

Tom Mercer

March 6th, 2005

As now I'm one of all my kind,
and you just symbol in this plot;
now take my vow that you are not,
and never will you be forgot –
though sadness here is all I find.

. . . .

20th September

Sigh, September, twilit sighs –
Shed not tears; they must fall
for whom September comes through veils;
They are an ever far-off dream –
Once unfolded in the sun.

. . . .

Ivy Oct. 15, '05

We marked the years
they went too fast
you made my days –
they would not last.

. . . .

Xmas '05

I celebrate for all I hold,
But grieve for all I hold;
I grieve but yet I celebrate,
but all in all I'm sad.

Ivy, March 6, 2006

It was a sad auf Wiedersehen;
but in my dreams you are again –
and in my heart will still remain.

. . . .

Ivy, September 20, '06

Not loud nor tuneful, but I sing
from deep within my heart;
how dear a good and faithful mate –
how sad when such must part.

. . . .

Ivy, October 15, '06

The summer seems so far away,
old Jack will have his wintry way –
but flood my heart with songs of May.

. . . .

Ivy, Xmas 06

I would the autumn leaves to stay
for ever – ever and a day.
Yet fall and fade, but not in vain –
So full and green to be again.
If only you my Ivy May.

Loving Husband
Bill

My poetry is not the realm

of they who , with an eye to fame ,

pretentiousness give rein ;

or with their thoughts

on pots of gold ,

flourish words that blind .

But that which would

explore the heart and probe the mind ,

and utilise such telling phrase

that seeks a like response .

Ferment , in truth ,

each vagrant thought

in untold , unknown minds .

Bill Hipkiss

Ulrike Thiel

Ridden

DRESSAGE FROM THE HORSE'S POINT OF VIEW

Translated by Coralie Hughes

J A Allen · London

First published in 2013 by
J. A. Allen
Clerkenwell House
45–47 Clerkenwell Green
London EC1R 0HT

J.A. Allen is an imprint of Robert Hale Ltd
www.allenbooks.co.uk

ISBN: 978-1-908809-08-7

Published simultaneously in the United States of America by
Trafalgar Square Books, North Pomfret, VT 05053, USA

Originally published in the German language as *Geritten werden* by Franckh-Kosmos Verlags-GmbH
& Co. KG, Stuttgart

Copyright © 2011 Franckh-Kosmos Verlags
English translation © 2013 Trafalgar Square Books

Disclaimer of Liability
The author and publisher shall have neither liability nor responsibility to any person or entity with
respect to any loss or damage caused or alleged to be caused directly or indirectly by the information
contained in this book. While the book is as accurate as the author can make it, there may be errors,
omissions, and inaccuracies.

J. A. Allen encourages the use of approved safety helmets in all equestrian sports and activities.

British Library Cataloging in Publication Data
A CIP record for this book is available from the British Library

All photos from the archives of Ulrike Thiel: p.1; 2 left, middle, right; 3 right; 5; 6 above; 7; 8 right;
left; 15; 19; 20 above; 20 below; 21 above, below; 22 above, below; 23 above left, above right; 23 below
left, below right; 24; 26; 28 above, below; 29 above, below; 30; 32 above left, middle, right; 32 below; 33
left, right; 33 below left, below right; 34; 35; 36; 37; 40; 41; 42; 46; 47; 53 below left, below right; 58; 61
above, below; 70 left; 72; 74; 76; 82; 84; 86 above, below; 87; 88; 89 above, below; 92 above; 94 left above,
middle, below; 96 left; 96 right; 103 above left, above right; 104 below; 106 above; 109; 110; 111; 112; 113
below left, below right; 114 above, below; 115 above, below; 116; 117; 118; 124; 125; 128; 129; 136; 137; 154;
156; 157; 158; 159; 160; 161; 162; 166; 167; 171 below; 177 above, below; 180; 185; 187; 188 above left; 190; 191
above; 198 above, below; 200 above; 202 above, below; 204 above, below; 205 above; 207; 209; 225.

80 color photographs from Horst Streitferdt / Kosmos for this book included: p. viii; x; 9; 10; 11; 12; 16;
17 left, middle, right; 39; 52 left; 52 right; 54; 60; 62; 68; 70 right; 71 left, middle, right; 80; 83; 92 below;
94 below; 95 above, below; 97; 98; 100; 103 left below, right below; 113 above left, above right; 120; 139;
140; 141; 142; 143; 144; 145; 146 (6); 147 (5); 148; 150; 151; 152 (6); 153 (6); 199 above; 200 below; 220; 224

More color photos from Jean Christen/Kosmos (1): p. 66; Creative collection (5): p. 55 below right; 56
above left, below; 57 above right, below; Klaus Jurgen Guni/ Kosmos (1): p. 13; Julia Rau/Kosmos (1): p.
77; Julia Rau (54): p. 14; 18 above, below; 25 left, right; 27; 38; 48; 50; 51 right; 55; 73; 78; 106 below; 107
below left, below right; 127; 130; 134 above, below; 135; 164 above, below; 165 above, below; 168; 169; 170;
171 above; 173; 175; 176 above, below; 178; 179; 180; 182; 183; 184; 188 below; 189; 191 below; 194; 199 below;
201; 205 below; 206; 211; 212; 213; 216; 217; Chrstiane Slawik/ Kosmos (1): p. 79; Horst Steitferdt (3): p.
172; 208; 214; Alexandra Zich/ Kosmos (19): p. vii; 3 left; 6 below; 44; 51 left; 59; 64; 65; 67; 69; 85; 93; 122
above, below; 123 left, right; 181; 210; 221.

Cover design by RM Didier
Typefaces: Vista Sans, Dolly, Proforma

Printed in China

Riding as a Harmonious Dialogue in Motion   1

Learning Together: How to Turn Horse and Human into Dance Partners   10

How the Dialogue in Motion Works   44

Mind-Body Learning in the Training of Horse and Rider   80

Foreword by Christine Stückelberger

In today's fast-paced world, many precious human values, such as sympathy and empathy for others, are lost. It is the age of quick success, regardless of the means, as seen in business worldwide. Money has become one of the most important factors of our time. You must achieve as much as possible, as quickly as possible. And how these goals are achieved is often questionable.

And that is exactly the point: these societal changes have come to affect riding. The traditional values of classical training are too slow, too hard to learn for many "trainers" or those who would like to be trainers. They don't bring success and easy money quickly enough. Like mushrooms, self-proclaimed "gurus" shoot up suddenly out of the ground with dubious training, and call themselves "classical."

It is unbelievable that a dressage method has been propagated that demands (quite literally) "blind obedience," even though such training is in every way at odds with what is best for the horse. In this method the horse, which is by nature a flight animal, has no means of evasion, no possibility of escaping the "predator." In nature, a horse balances himself "up and out"—meaning, he carries his neck as a balancing rod high and proud, and usually with a positioning toward the outside of a turn or bend. This can be seen when he is loose out in the pasture, or when he is worked on the circle in the arena without side reins.

Training with his head pulled in to his chest, on the other hand, creates fear, tension, loss of trust, and ultimately physical and psychological damage. Yet the Fédération Equestre Internationale (FEI) looks on without action. Even worse, many medals are given to horses trained in such a torturous way. And, it turns the training of dressage horses into a farce when a horse trained in such a way is proclaimed the "Happiest Horse of the Year."

It is critical that brave individuals continue to shed light on the evils of "modern" dressage. I would like to heartily thank Dr. Ulrike Thiel for her courage in writing a book on this controversial subject, and I encourage her to continue to write and educate others. Horses need an "attorney"—someone to lobby for their best interests. With the horse in mind, it is not possible to give the public too much information. Despite pressure from others and threats, Dr. Thiel has brought this work—her second book—to reality. My admiration and my personal gratitude should tell her that she doesn't stand alone in the battle to save classical riding. She has now many passionate supporters, and after this book, she will surely have more.

Christine Stückelberger

Dressage World Champion and Olympian committed to the fair treatment of horses in sport.

Christine Stückelberger with her mare Ravenna.

Preface

As I worked on my first book *Die Psyche des Pferdes*, my German publisher and I recognized the potential for a subsequent volume in which I would examine more deeply the horse's experience under correct classical training. We wanted to shed some light on "being ridden" from the horse's viewpoint. I would incorporate psychological as well as technical aspects of horse training, including the physical and mental learning processes that the horse experiences and possibly deems as pleasant or unpleasant.

And so began the critical study that led to this book on various dressage training methods and how they are experienced by the horse. My work with my students, my own research and observations—at both the lower and upper levels of the sport—made it apparent to me that a systematic comparison of how different ways of riding affect the horse would be useful to those facing a choice in trainers and training methods. In addition, it is important to me that

Ulrike Thiel with the six-year-old Tamaselli (Royal Dance x Izmir).

I explain to the horse enthusiast—whether a rider or not—how sensible classical training protects the horse. We must learn to ask ourselves how so many "modern" training methods can appear to bring success while being, at best, unpleasant to the horse, and doing him more harm than good.

Unfortunately, not everything described as "classical," "horse-friendly," or "natural" lives up to the label. The educated equestrian historian also recognizes old concepts being touted today as "modern," "state-of-the-art," and "scientifically supported." Old concepts are dressed in "new clothes" and sold under new slogans. We must remember that in the history of man and horse, spanning thousands of years, there is little that hasn't already been tried in our drive to turn the horse into a riding animal, to dominate him, or in the best sense, to create a dance partner.

Even the rider with the best of intentions finds it difficult to make his way through the jungle of methods available today. Riding in a horse-friendly manner requires a large personal investment on the part of the rider and the trainer. Learning to ride correctly frequently forces the rider to confront her own weaknesses, which can only be overcome with maturity and positive self-criticism. It is easier to blame the horse and to use all sorts of gadgets and techniques in order to avoid such responsibility.

Every horse enthusiast should strive to understand what helps and what hurts the horse by gaining the necessary knowledge about the nature of horses—his capabilities, his anatomy and biomechanics—as well as his psychological and physical preparedness for training. The rider must learn to feel and sense what the horse tells her as they work together, and she must be willing to analyze the information he provides critically and logically. Do we want the horse to experience us as a partner? Or as a dominating presence—even as a predator on his back? We can decide! With this book, I hope to make this decision a little easier for you.

Dr. Ulrike Thiel

Riding as a Harmonious Dialogue in Motion

From Prey Animal to Dance Partner

For centuries we have used horses as a form of transportation—under saddle or in front of a wagon. Many children draw their first horses with a saddle on their back because "horses" and "riding" are synonymous to them. We should consider, however, that horses were no more "created" to be ridden than we were created to be riders, skiers, musicians, or astronauts.

1

2

1–2 Ancient artworks frequently show the horse carrying a rider or pulling a wagon as if it were the most natural thing in the world for the horse to be man's subject.

As we shall see, man and horse are born with instincts and natural patterns of behavior that make being a rider and being ridden difficult. Luckily, there are other characteristics present that enable you to become a rider and your horse to learn to carry you on his back and work with you while you're there. Man and horse have sufficient physical and mental capabilities to allow them to grow beyond merely dealing forcefully with each other and to instead develop a true dialogue in motion with one another. This dialogue in motion is similar to dancing, and it can bring both partners a sense of peace, great joy, and limitless physical development and mental growth.

1
2
3

1–3 It is interesting how when children first come to a therapeutic riding class, they almost always draw a horse with a rider in the saddle (1). Later, once they have gotten to know their therapy horses, they draw themselves with "their" horses differently (2 and 3).

Horse and rider "melt" into each other, two separate beings but inextricably linked.

The ideal is NOT a centaur with a human head, with the human making all the decisions.

The path to a dialogue in motion

Classical training that is correct for the horse is a systematic and clearly marked path, leading to a dialogue in motion with the horse. As in a dance, there is a leading partner and a following partner. In the ideal dance, both partners experience equal joy as they "float across the floor" together. Each listens to the other, considers the other's needs and movement, and ultimately enjoys achieving coordinated motion. This "dance" has long been the goal of classical equestrian art, and classically correct riding instruction can still achieve it.

In classical philosophy, horse and rider become one—"They melt into each other," as Johann Wolfgang von Goethe described it. Mythology presents us with the picture of the centaur, where horse and man share one body. But in the ideal, the rider shouldn't become the dominant head. The horse should be allowed to think, as well. His contribution should be respected and valued. Being ridden should not be at his cost.

Both man and horse can reach a spiritual level in a dialogue of motion where they actually do, in essence, "melt" into one another. In the ideal, they decide together what must be done next, although the rider provides the direction, and the horse takes this direction and translates it into movement out of his own desire to do so. The horse can also make suggestions, which are usually reasonable, since the horse is the best judge of which movements are technically possible in a given situation, and which are not. In this way, the rider can help the horse and the horse the rider in accomplishing movements.

Dancing together rather than sparring

Unlike in general pleasure riding, classically correct dressage is not about getting from Point A to Point B as comfortably or as quickly as possible, with the horse as man's servant in the process. It is about the rider moving with the horse according to certain rules in a way that is:

· dynamic, yet
· controlled, and
· aesthetically pleasing to the eye, and
· optimally protective of muscles, tendons, bones, and joints of both horse and rider.

In the process, the rider supports the horse and accepts responsibility for their motion together, while the horse has the more dynamic role, requiring great strength and flexibility in the exercise at hand, which both accomplish together. Riding, and especially dressage, should never degrade into some form of battle, in which one partner domi-

Horse and rider join together in a dialogue of motion.

1

2

1 – 2 *Dressage and dancing the Tango have more in common than one might presume. Despite both dressage partners having different jobs (the rider leads and supports, the horse takes direction and responds with movement), they ideally "melt" together into a single unit to perform an exercise, such as the shoulder-in.*

nates the other and forces him with a strong grip to do exactly what is wanted (and without considering the repercussions).

They are still horses, despite the rider on their back

A well-known saying goes like this: *A horse without a rider is still a horse, a rider without a horse is only a man.*

Dressage should carefully follow the rule that a ridden horse should, above all, still remain a horse. He should be able to move like a horse, feel like a horse, and only be requested to work with man in observance of his nature as a horse. The horse should not be expected to conform exclusively to the needs of man, which unfortunately happens in many riding disciplines. The needs of the horse should extend beyond his basic care and feeding to also include how you interact and work with him.

Correct classical dressage works exclusively through the horse's natural movement. The horse should show expressiveness and joy in his movement. Motion is, in fact, how the horse can tell us about his degree of inner comfort and the state of his emotions. Consequently, we should not force the horse into movements or postures that are contrary to his nature and uncomfortable for him. Of course, we must help nature a little since the horse must adjust mentally and physically to the unnatural state of having a rider on his back.

Empathizing with the horse

In order to achieve a harmonious dialogue of motion, the rider must put herself "in her horse's shoes"—she must empathize with the horse. This enables the rider to optimally support the horse as a true partner. The horse will then willingly follow the rider and try to do what the rider asks of him, despite it being sometimes difficult. The rider will know the horse trusts her because she obviously understands him, is considerate of his needs, and can support him technically.

Seen in this way, dressage is about partnership, relationship, communication, feeling, and working together to accomplish movement. We must always remember that the horse without a rider on his back isn't confronted with the need to perform specific exercises; in fact, the horse can move quite well without a rider.

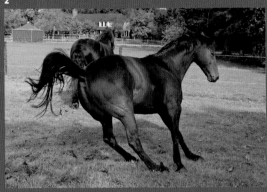

1–4 *When allowed time to play together, horses develop friendships, keep fit, and learn how to respond to the movement suggestions of a partner. Free movement in the pasture is an important factor in the horse's mental and physical health.*

1   2   3

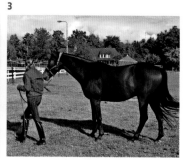

1–3 *We should become the horse's trusted partner. Even when we take him away from the security of the herd, he should gladly come with us.*

Fluid Motion Rather than Ruthless Domination

We all know the feeling of closeness and joy when we find ourselves moving fluidly with a horse. It is a heavenly feeling when a horse goes well beneath us and we form a single moving unit with him, when everything simply "works." Yes, there are moments in riding when we can literally feel "high." But, as with a true addiction, the high doesn't happen frequently enough and is often followed by a "dry spell," which we must get through because we want to experience that "kick" again. Luckily for riders, "addiction" to oneness with the horse is entirely legal, and we can seek out ways to find this happy feeling again and therefore continue to progress in our partnership with our horse. Hopefully, our horse experiences a reciprocal happiness in our dialogue of motion. I am convinced that it is possible.

Throughout history there have been humans who didn't care how the horse felt when ridden. We have, at times, admired such "horse tamers" more than those who worked with horses in a quieter and less spectacular way. Even today, in our "horse friendly" society, these tendencies are still apparent.

We can see evidence in how the ridden horse moves. For example, a horse free in a pasture with friends "passages" when he is excited about something and wants to say to his herdmates, "Look at me! Look what I can do!" When a horse is forced to passage via dominant riding, then he may demonstrate passage-like steps, but the natural joyful expression of the instinctual movement is lacking. A movement that is naturally connected to a positive sense of excitement is suddenly turned into a forced behavior that is both unpleasant and

Both riding partners can learn to enjoy harmonious motion together.

cramped. Not only does this damage the horse mentally, it can cause physical issues, since forced, tense steps are biomechanically problematic.

Historically, heroic depictions of "horse tamers" show that forcefully subduing a horse has been (and in some cases still is) completely acceptable in many societies.

Riding in a way that is best for the horse is not easy

In order to ride in a manner that is best for the horse, the rider must be prepared to continually critique herself—her seat, how she uses her body, her motivations, and her general attitude toward riding. She must consistently reflect on how she influences the horse, and she must steadily work to improve herself and her relationship with her horse. She must understand the Classical Training Scale and have

1

2

1–2 *Domination of the horse—past and present.*

internalized the logic behind it. She must also believe in her horse, like him, and let him know that she does!

Another well-known saying states, "A man's life is too short to learn to ride well." This is confirmed over and over, time and again. Learning to ride in a way that is good for the horse is not easy. It is a complex mind-body endeavor that requires extreme body control and coordination. Riding also requires psychological abilities that we don't require to such an extent in our everyday life.

The rider should always let her horse know that she likes him and that she trusts him.

Learning Together: How to Turn Horse and Human into Dance Partners

Social Partnership of Two Dissimilar Beings

At first, horse and rider seem unlikely to be able to work well together
due to their different instinctive behavior patterns. The horse is a
flight animal (prey), while man is historically a predator who nevertheless may stiffen or freeze when in danger, and react anxiously when
losing control. Let's look first more closely at those characteristics of a
horse that make it hard for him to be ridden and then the characteristics in a human that can help the horse experience being ridden as a
pleasure rather than as a form of punishment or as a burden.

Learn to bridge natural instincts through trust

When a horse feels something on his back he instinctually senses his
life is threatened. In nature, it would normally only be a predator that
would be on his back, and that would indeed be a threat to his life.
Therefore, it is only logical that the horse defends himself from anything on his back.

*The horse's instinctual reaction
to danger is flight. He must
learn to trust having someone
on his back, in a position the
horse senses as life-threatening.*

Because of the prey-predator relationship, the horse can be started under saddle according to predatory principles. Or instead of choosing to brutally suppress the horse's spirit, we can use horse-friendly training techniques. The latter take longer but can ultimately overcome the horse's natural flight and defensive instincts. The horse's social abilities are such that he can learn to trust his rider, just as he trusts his four-legged friends in his herd.

Humans don't automatically know how to ride. As mentioned, we tend to react fearfully to large movements over which we don't personally have control, usually by stiffening and "freezing." It takes a human an entire riding lifetime to overcome this fear and the instinct to stiffen.

We must understand that it is a big psychological challenge for the horse (as a prey animal) to not perceive the rider as a threat that he must get rid of as quickly as possible. When on the horse's back, the rider is in one of the horse's blind spots. The horse can feel her but not see her. The horse is given information via the rider's body contact that he must then interpret. He must determine that the rider on his

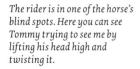

The rider is in one of the horse's blind spots. Here you can see Tommy trying to see me by lifting his head high and twisting it.

In some cases, the horse's prey instinct is deliberately triggered, such as in rodeo bronc competition.

back doesn't want to cause him to fall down (by upsetting his balance), doesn't want to slit his belly open (with spurs that seem like claws), doesn't want to take away his ability to escape danger (through restrictive devices that inhibit flight), and doesn't otherwise want to cause him pain (in the mouth, neck, poll, or back) of the sort that might precede being killed.

Although the horse's flight instinct is often successfully suppressed through brute force, as in old-fashioned "horse-breaking" techniques, it remains permanently active in his subconscious. This causes the horse a high degree of stress and stands in the way of a relaxed mind, supple body, and healthy movement. I must note here that forceful horse-breaking is still found throughout the world, and sometimes even under the guise of "natural horsemanship," or another such catch-phrase that camouflages what actually happens—namely the subjugation of the horse by overwhelming him with physical and psychological pressure and pain. For the horse, it is the equivalent of a predator sitting on his back, sparing his life for the moment, but perfectly capable of killing him at any time.

Becoming partners in play

The more respectful way of working with and riding a horse is to motivate him to enjoy the movements you explore together. This should flow out of a relationship built on trust and positive experiences. Motion is what enables the horse to stay fit as a flight animal. He associates moving with playtime in the pasture with his herd-mates, and it makes him feel good. This good feeling in the body is very important.

When playing together with our horse, in motion, we build an intensely positive relationship with him, giving him the security to experience the learning process as something pleasant and without stress. This helps "quiet" his prey-animal instincts.

This is what riding looks like when shared movement brings the same joy to both horse and rider.

When the horse experiences riding as a social interaction, then the mental and physical participation that we require from him in dressage makes sense to him. With appropriate and quality training, he quickly notices that he can benefit through his relationship with his rider. This feeds the motivation that can help bring the horse to superior performance. When appreciation is shown by the rider, the horse's achievements fuel his self-confidence and generate a sense of physical well-being in the horse (movement feels good).

My horses like to be ridden or longed. They show me this all the time. Sometimes they line up and want to be the next one to come in for a lesson. When I find that one doesn't want to leave the pasture and go to work, then I know I have done something wrong in training, or I have discouraged him, or I have otherwise damaged our relationship and must correct it as quickly as possible.

What Horse and Rider Must Achieve

In order to become a dressage horse (a role that, of course, the horse never requested), the horse must adjust to a complex interplay between mind and body. Mind-body concepts can help the rider have empathy for the horse in this scenario. We can compare the complex

Mind-body Skills
When I say "mind-body skills" I mean the reciprocal learning processes between the mind and the body when working out complex physical movements. Psychological processes influence movement and vice a versa. In both riding and being ridden, mind and body of the rider and the horse must work together in a similar way. They must work together in order to be able to meet new movement challenges. We must always consider the difficulties the horse might have with something that, from our perspective, seems "simple."

Horses at liberty can demonstrate movement qualities they have learned through systematic training. Here, Resi reaches powerfully forward with her inside hind leg as she turns, and her energetic canter goes decidedly uphill. This shows me that what she has learned in several years of training under saddle she finds to be reasonable and useful when running free.

Just as a blind man must integrate the use of a walking stick so as to have a new sense of his body, where it begins and ends, so must the horse learn to incorporate the rider on his back. In the case of the blind man, it is ideal when the walking stick becomes practically like his own hand. In the same way, the rider should become an extension of the horse, but this can only happen when she doesn't disturb the horse and supports him actively in a dialogue of motion.

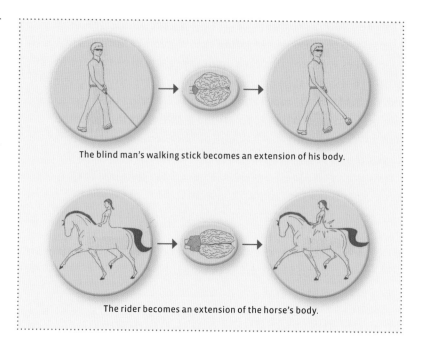

The blind man's walking stick becomes an extension of his body.

The rider becomes an extension of the horse's body.

mind-body skills necessary for the horse to perform when ridden to those we need in activities such as skiing, gymnastics, and ballet (for example). These sports make similar demands on our mind and body that being ridden does on the horse. (Later in this book we will compare these activities, and it will convince you of the necessity of a systematic process for training the dressage horse.)

My riding students have much better understanding for the horse and better respect for what a dressage horse must figure out and achieve once I have them try a few special body exercises that help them feel their way through new movement sequences or different ways of communicating (see more about this on p. 32).

Subtle movements of the rider communicate her sensitivity and her intentions to the horse.

The rider as coach

With a rider on his back, the horse has to cope with an additional load that shouldn't be underestimated. It is a big transition to perform the same movements with a rider that he can do freely on his own. Instinctive patterns of motion that are part of the social and emotional context of the herd are taken out of that context by the rider on his back, who now directs his movements. Although correct dressage training is based on how the horse moves naturally, in order to perform required exercises, the horse must adjust how he usually moves, find a new balance, and become physically stronger. He must also adjust mentally to the role of a dressage horse. The rider, therefore, must be psychologist, fitness trainer, and coach—but above all, a partner and a person the horse trusts. The rider should help the horse learn to express himself in the dialogue of motion, try to understand what the horse wants to tell her, and then incorporate that message into the training.

Developing a new body awareness

Just as a person that is learning a new sport has to internalize new patterns of movement, so must the horse in the course of dressage training. The horse must load a new body image onto his "internal hard drive" (his nervous system)—one of himself with a rider on his back. A blind person must develop a new sense of his body that includes his walking stick; the horse experiences a similar challenge. As he becomes a dressage horse, he must develop a second sense of self, and this new body awareness becomes only more complex as training progresses. Control of old and integration of new patterns of movement occur when new nerve connections are made in the nervous system. As the horse changes physically, his brain and nervous system must continue to develop, as well.

During the horse's development we must help him learn to associate pleasant feelings with his work. The more positive the individual "tiles" of the training "mosaic," the easier it is for the horse to access

The dialogue of motion enables the horse to "tell" his rider what is going on inside him (the horse), for example:

1 Tommy (the horse) sees something and doesn't know if he should fear it or not.

2 Although the rider may instinctively want to correct Tommy's hesitation with her hands, it isn't the best way to keep his focus and connection.

3 Instead, if the rider indicates with her seat to keep cantering, Tommy will seek the contact again on his own.

1

2

3

This rider is clearly communicating to her horse that she is not willing to consider his needs during their training session.

newly learned patterns of movement from his hard drive and employ them when performing a new exercise with the rider.

When new tasks are accomplished in a positive context, and without pain, tension, or aggression on the part of the rider, the horse will experience the work you do together as pleasant. He will then be happy to switch on his "riding horse frame" as soon as he is tacked up.

Building the necessary musculature

Untrained horses tense quickly when carrying a rider for a number of reasons: because their musculature is not accustomed to the rider's weight, because they tire easily, or even because they are in pain. The tense horse becomes not only uncomfortable for the rider to ride, but also can suffer injuries of the support and movement apparatus: the tendons, joints, and muscles.

Perhaps you are a well-trained athlete accustomed to jogging 3 miles a couple times a week; those 3 miles would be a totally different thing if you jogged them one day with a 50-pound bag of oats on your

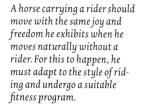

A horse carrying a rider should move with the same joy and freedom he exhibits when he moves naturally without a rider. For this to happen, he must adapt to the style of riding and undergo a suitable fitness program.

Work on the longe line serves to prepare the muscles, tendons, and joints so they are ready to carry the rider.

back. I am sure that you wouldn't find the experience enjoyable and that you would probably have a huge muscle cramp afterward.

In order to jog 3 miles as comfortably with a load as without, you must first change your running style (how you move) and begin with short sessions that build toward the longer one. You will do even better when you prepare for your load by doing strength training in the gym in advance.

The horse also needs such fitness training prior to work under saddle. As we shall see, the responsible trainer can help the horse develop his natural physical and mental capabilities through systematic exercises, including those that establish patterns of motion on the longe line, in hand, and under saddle. The goal of classical riding was to create an equine work of art—the horse should be developed

Horses at liberty load the forehand heavily and change directions by leaning, stretching the neck out for balance.

aesthetically, just like a ballet dancer. And, in correct, modern classical riding, we strive for the horse to enjoy becoming an equine work of art.

With the added weight of the rider on his back, the horse must balance himself completely differently so that the forehand is not overloaded.

Finding a new balance under the load of the rider

Much like a wheelbarrow, the horse naturally puts more weight on the forehand, as his back is not really made to carry weight. But when he is ridden, we don't want the horse to move with his weight "downhill" or "heavy on the forehand." As riders who plan to sit on a back that is not made to support our weight to begin with, we must think of ways to overcome the "undesirable" distribution of weight that is the horse's natural means of load-bearing.

Movements that were once natural to the horse become suddenly very tiring when a rider is on his back because it changes his balance. The natural bearing of weight by the forehand is increased, which makes changes of direction more difficult. The rider's weight also moves around in a way that is not helpful to the horse. And so, a new balance must be developed—the horse must learn a different way of controlling his own movement and distributing his weight and the rider's in order to effectively support the rider.

Riding theory teaches us that we can help the horse accomplish this new balance through work on straightening, collection, and lateral and longitudinal bend. Skills in these areas help the horse move in a way that protects his muscles and joints while carrying the rider smoothly and efficiently.

Balance exercises for the rider

Try these two exercises to help better understand what it is like for the horse to have the weight and movement of the rider on his back while trying to perform dressage movements: carry a child on your shoulders as you move forward, backward, and turn; or, balance a 6-foot hollow, plastic pole (PVC works) from the building supply store on the flat of one hand while you "walk," "trot," and "canter" straight and on turns. These exercises quickly show you the challenges that confront a dressage horse. You will find you need to use both hands to balance your "load," and when turning, you'll have to lessen the degree of the curve. Your attempts to keep your load balanced may cause you to deviate from your planned path, and you will find you have difficulty maintaining a steady tempo.

I always have my students try the pole exercise. They quickly come to understand why their horse does unexpected things like, for example, falling to the outside, going too fast, or shortening his stride. They also learn how hard they must concentrate on the pole (when they first attempt the exercise) and how it moves on curves to such a degree that they frequently bump into objects in the arena or other students.

After a little practice it isn't as difficult to balance the pole. It starts to be fun to run faster or slower, to move sideways, and to do "canter transitions" and "pirouettes." This exercise helps you develop a new body awareness—you move from just "me" to "me with a pole"—and this enables you to develop the ability to move as elastically with the pole as you can without it.

1 *It is a good exercise to carry a child on your shoulders and see how it affects your ability to move and turn. When the child sits quietly, he is easy to carry.*

2 *However, when the child moves, you must be able to quickly adjust your balance under his weight.*

Balance Exercise for the Rider

Moving while balancing a pole on the flat of one hand can help you understand the process the horse goes through under the rider. When you first attempt the exercise, it is difficult to balance the pole and your body. You may have to use your other arm to stabilize yourself.

Eventually, you grow accustomed to carrying the pole and can "trot" and "canter" with it. The pole, in effect, becomes an extension of your body.

When the pole is not symmetrically balanced, as shown here, it causes stiffening in several areas of the body (noted by the arrows). Your resulting movements are abrupt, which is hard on your joints.

When changing direction or speed with the pole, you must again rebalance, or stiffness is the result (see arrows). It is difficult to move as you may have planned, which can be frustrating.

When carrying a rider who sits crookedly, the horse must constantly react to the unbalanced weight of the rider. This again causes stiffness and tension, interfering with his ability to execute movements as he may be capable.

When the rider doesn't sit straight, the horse is forced to stiffen in multiple areas of the body to compensate (see arrows). Over time this goes beyond discomfort while being ridden and leads to temporary injury or permanent physical damage.

Uncomfortable crookedness

The pole-balancing exercise becomes immediately uncomfortable when the "neutral" balanced pole is replaced with one that weighs more on one end. When you repeat the exercise with such a pole, you will find you must constantly brace your body. Plus, you are forced to concentrate on keeping the pole steady, rather than where you are going and how you are moving. This leads to movement that is less elastic and less pleasant, and if you do the exercise long enough, you will feel your wrist, neck, shoulder, and hip on one side stiffen against the imbalance and seem "overloaded."

This is what happens to the horse when he is carrying a rider who sits crookedly; who doesn't yet have control of her own asymmetry; or who is uncoordinated and can't stay centered. Consider the contrast between working with the evenly weighted pole (which you began with) and the unbalanced pole—the exercise is much more pleasant (even fun!) when the pole is balanced. It is the same for the horse when working with a rider. And, since the horse is a flight animal, he is particularly uncomfortable when he feels out of balance since it affects his ability to flee in the face of danger.

The rider becomes a part of the horse's "movement system"

As riders, we can make it easy or especially hard for a horse to learn how to move and to be coordinated in that movement. If we don't want to be an irritating burden for him, we should strive to always sit straight, vertical, and in the middle of the horse, in accordance with the classical seat. We must ride turns, lateral movements, and transitions without leaning sideways or backward.

The crooked rider interferes with the horse's balance.

Learning and practicing complex movement patterns

Most of us know how tiring it is when first trying to learn a complex new mind-body skill, such as driving a car. Later, once we have learned and internalized the sequence of events and can remember them as needed, and when we have practiced enough, what was hard and exhausting becomes easy for us. In the case of driving a car, we must still concentrate on steering and on the traffic, but we don't have to think about every time we need to accelerate or shift.

The experience is similar when we learn another sport, say for

1–2 *Here you can see a rider who is intentionally not centered as he uses his body to tell the horse to change leads.*

example, skiing. Skiing is like driving in that we have to learn new movement sequences; however, skiing also requires focused physical training of our muscles. Our physical condition and ability to react must be developed. While driving a car doesn't require us to strengthen our thigh muscles, skiing requires conditioning before we head to the slopes.

Moreover, the skier must learn and practice certain movements under different circumstances: skiing in powder requires different techniques than skiing on ice, for example. In order to safely make a steep, slick descent with some control and grace, you must have trained regularly and have the necessary physical and mental preparedness. To head straight to the slope from the desk without training quickly leads to injuries.

When I think about my first attempts to go, stop, and turn on skis, I can easily understand how hard a horse must concentrate when on the longe early in his training and asked by his trainer to quietly move into a canter. He must find a way of balancing on the circle that is completely different from how he would naturally turn corners.

Together, through a dialogue in motion, horse and rider build a new mind-body image where they become an extension of one another.

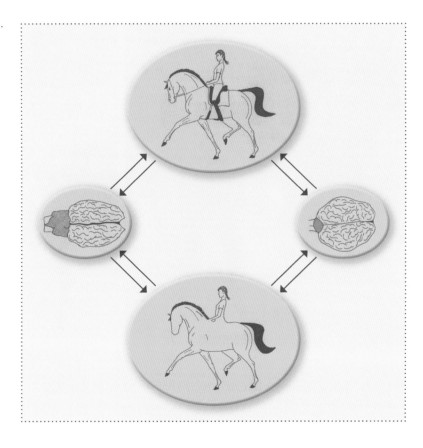

"Training" means the development of physical abilities so that the talent of the horse evolves and his weaknesses are improved upon. Demands on certain organs (such as the heart, for example) must be increased sensibly.

In turn, the rider must develop minimal endurance, speed, and power, but a great deal of coordination and suppleness. When dressage is compared to ballet, the rider would be the ballerina: her coordination and fine motor skills are of primary importance. It is a little different for the horse. He must primarily bring endurance, speed, and power to the partnership, as well as grace and coordination. In a way the horse is like the male ballet dancer, who likewise needs more power and jumping strength than the female partner, whom he must be able to carry.

Just as the human learning to ski must learn to move and balance with two boards strapped to his feet, so must the horse learn to move and balance with the addition of a rider on his back.

Value of diverse sport experiences

As riders and trainers we can more easily understand how our horses feel physically when being ridden if we have experience with other sports that require a high degree of coordination and the systematic development of flexibility, speed, power, and endurance. Some good examples include skiing and ballet (which I've already mentioned), as well as gymnastics and vaulting. When we have participated in such activities, we understand how muscle cramps feel and how fatigue affects the muscles and coordination needed during performance. We can then avoid expecting our horses to work when in pain or fatigued.

I believe that any rider who wants more than just a horse as a mode of transportation from here to there, but who also wants to support her horse and to teach him something new, should have significant

Vaulting is ideal preparation for the rider as it allows her to experience all the different aspects of a coordinated sport and therefore to identify with the horse's experience when ridden.

Warming Up is Necessary for Supple Riding

I WAS PREVIOUSLY A SKI INSTRUCTOR, *and I have played a lot of basketball and tennis, as well as done gymnastics. I am a certified sports instructor and spent many hours training to become a riding and vaulting instructor. Presently I exercise a lot during the daily work on my farm, plus I go to the gym, swim on a regular basis, and run three to four times a week for 4 to 6 miles. I do all this to stay fit for riding, keep my body centered, improve joint flexibility, and prepare my muscles for use.*

experience with at least one other sport that requires coordination, endurance, and power on her part. She should also engage in other sports in addition to riding in order to remain fit and to truly understand the feeling of physical exertion that the horse experiences. I find that vaulting is ideal as a form of preparation for the rider, as it requires the same elements of physical exertion that confront the horse when he is ridden. And running reminds the rider how unpleasant hard, uneven, or slippery ground feels, as well as how unsettling a slip or bad step can be.

Targeted training

About a year ago I decided to run a half-marathon and prepared for seven months with a running group. I had to improve my running style and develop my endurance for the race through different types of training. After running, cooling down was required, which was a new experience for me. This kind of targeted training taught me a lot that I found could be applied to my role as a rider and trainer. As a result, I am more alert for signs of fatigue in my horses. I have felt in

When we train for and participate in a sporting event such as a half-marathon or marathon, we come to understand the importance of strength and endurance training, as well as incorporating a warm-up and cool-down period, in the training of our dressage horse.

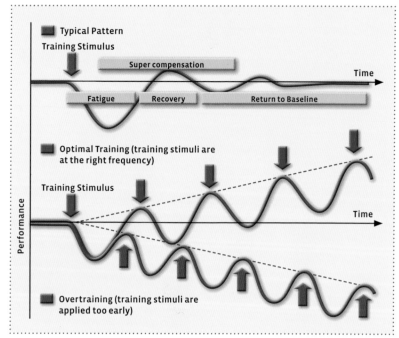

my own body how important stretching, warming up, and cooling down are. Additionally, I have experienced how finding the right rhythm and the right running technique leads to a pleasant physical sensation during and after a run. I had to learn to focus so as to maintain my own rhythm even when other runners with a different running rhythm got very close to me. This is something that the horse also experiences, for example, when schooling in a crowded warm-up ring or when competing in group classes.

My experience training for a half-marathon taught me more about the power and endurance required of a dressage horse. And it proved how important it is to train the horse in a way that is physiologically correct, with regular warm-up and cool-down periods.

Through our own athletic experiences, we understand why developing physical ability step by step with breaks in training can be successful. We understand why we can't expect the same level of effort after a break from a well-trained horse as was initially put forth, and we know that you have to carefully work back up to the previous level of effort. Moreover, we are conscious of the importance of external and internal motivation. The horse will only put forth a truly honest effort when he enjoys his work and is not hindered by pain, fatigue, or insufficient conditioning.

Comparing rider and horse

The rider must go through very complex mind-body development as she evolves from a bipedal being to a rider. She must overcome the natural human instinct to stiffen in the face of danger (see p. 12). Learning to ride well provides insight into the battle between right- and left-sidedness of the whole body, as well as the mental stress that results when trying to develop symmetrical movement. It requires learning independent control of individual body parts, which enables systematic and coordinated movement.

The rider experiences in her own learning process all the same problems the horse copes with as he becomes a dressage horse.

In contrast to the horse, the rider must primarily learn to coordinate micro-movements of her body while the horse learns to execute large patterns.

In her role as both the one being carried and the leading dance

The rider and horse should be partners in a dance, each sensitive to the other's movements.

1

2

3

1–4 This exercise helps the rider understand the process of learning coordination and how to work the muscles on turns. When the rider tries to make a turn on all fours, she notices how much coordination and power the same movement requires of the horse. Try again to "ride" a turn on your own two feet while keeping that understanding you acquired on all fours.

4

partner, the rider must be able to employ minimal movements that are precise and at the right intensity for the horse. These impulses motivate the horse to adjust his own movement plan to accommodate the wishes of the rider. In riding theory we know the combination of such movement impulses as "aids." Since the horse has the primary responsibility for mobility, power, and endurance in carrying out the rider's instructions, or rather "suggestions," the experience a rider has while riding is not comparable to what a horse experiences when being ridden.

For example, learning to balance on a turn with the additional weight of the rider on his back is different for the horse than it is for the rider riding the movement. His experience is more comparable in level of difficulty to the rider's attention to maintaining an independent and elastic seat. Add to this the need to carry out specific instructions as directed by the rider while in the turn, and you begin to see the challenge the horse faces during each moment of a ride.

Additionally, the rider and the horse must activate and control their trunk and leg muscles completely differently. The rider sits vertically on the horse and must learn to hold herself in balance from the core (stomach, back, and hips) so as to not disturb the horse's movement and to be able to give necessary instructions. The horse, on the other hand, must learn to swing his legs from a horizontal, raised back (that is hopefully relaxed) while coping with the added weight of

1

2

1–2 *The rider should have the same independent, coordinated control and symmetry of her body that the ballet dancer achieves after years of training in front of a mirror. This enables the rider to give the horse correct signals and support from the saddle.*

the rider. This requires intentional development of the right musculature in the horse.

In later chapters we will use physical exercises and comparisons with other sports to better understand how the horse feels when ridden, as well as what helps him, what bothers him, and what damages him.

1

2

1 *The horse moves with a horizontal, raised, and (hopefully) relaxed back. Carrying the rider is only possible when the horse's back "opens" and arches from the withers, when his haunches flex, and when he steps actively under his body.*

2 *When in the saddle, the rider must maintain a vertical and straight vertebral column, preserving the back's natural "S" shape, while keeping independent control of her other body parts.*

1

2

1-2 "Tommy" the foal learns how to go through a plastic curtain—he follows his mother's lead even though he is afraid of it.

How the Horse Learns

As a flight animal, the horse has at his disposal extremely keen body awareness, significant physical ability, social intelligence, and a good memory. It would be a mistake on our part not to consider these attributes in the course of training him to be a dressage horse. The horse is far superior to the human in his ability to learn to move, as well as to control his movement, power, speed, and endurance. Classical training intends to actively encourage the horse to employ this "physical intelligence."

Muscle memory and social intelligence

We frequently hear horses described as "dumb animals." Horses are exactly as intelligent as they need to be for their natural function. That just means that they think differently than we do. They have a large brain capacity and an excellent memory, which can sometimes be pretty unpleasant for us riders since horses easily notice when we haven't done something right. Horses try to find a relationship between different events, and their problem-solving ability is focused on issues that they are most likely to confront in their natural environment.

Horses have extremely good muscle memory. I have experienced this often with horses brought to me for retraining after having been "pulled together" by their riders for years. I try to give the horse and his rider a pleasant riding experience together, but as soon as the horse is asked to assume a body position that he previously experienced as unpleasant or painful, he tenses, gets excited, spooks, or gets confused. Certain body postures or movements associated with unpleasant experiences reawaken related emotions.

The social intelligence of horses is also especially highly developed. When we compare the brain of dogs, cows, people, and horses we notice distinct variations. For example, certain ancient brain structures are more developed in the horse than in humans since instincts naturally play a greater role in the horse. Furthermore, the differentiation of the cortex in the horse is more distinct than in the dog or cow.

Horses are relationship animals

Horses are socially oriented because in nature, the herd means security. Horses learn from the other members of the herd and seek harmony in their social relationships with others of their kind. Horses behave the same way with "their" human; they can grow to trust their trainer as they would their herd leader.

Horses also love physical play with other horses; such interaction allows them to stay in tune with their body and stay fit, which is important for a flight animal. Physical play teaches them to react fast and provides body awareness in three-dimensional space and in motion. Physical play reduces stress in the life of a horse—a stressed horse can neither learn nor improve his physical condition.

Horses are socially oriented. They seek relationships with others that provide physical contact.

Horses nurture intense friend-ships with others of their kind.

Learning in the relationship

When we humans can build on the horse's natural strengths, achiev-ing a relationship of trust as a partner in physical activity, then we have a good chance of learning to "dance" with our horse. The horse can only bring all his physical and mental capabilities actively to the training process when the relationship he has with his rider is a positive one.

Learning in a relationship is a bit different than pure stimulus-response learning (such as teaching conditioned responses to a rider's aids). Actively thinking through how to do a task as a horse-and-rider partnership involves an entirely different set of emotional and neuro-motor learning and development processes.

When the rider wants to achieve an active movement dialogue with the horse, then she must clearly understand both the positive and the negative influence (whether intentional or not) that she can have on the horse's ability to move and on his mental state. She must give the horse a chance to understand what she is asking and then consciously plan his movements. We don't want the horse to merely

Strong social connections with human partners are also possible.

react to us as we are riding; we want him to think and work with us as an active partner in a dance.

Unfortunately, old-fashioned aspects of behavioral learning theory persist in the horse business, I think more so than in any other area. We often act according to the behaviorist approach, where every horse (the "learner") is a "black box"—it does not matter that nothing is known about what goes on inside the box, because it simply requires conditioning the horse to stimulus-response on the outside to train him.

Even a newborn foal can trust a human like his own kind.

Behaviorism
The term "behaviorism" comes from the work of behavioral psychologist John B. Watson, among others. Classical behaviorism focuses on stimulus-response learning. The learning organism is seen as the so-called "black box," which reacts to every change in the environment (stimulus) with an activity (response).

A good relationship can be a reward for the horse

When we want to motivate a horse to do something, we must first nurture a good relationship with him. It is just like the intricate relationship development that occurs between a mare and foal, or older herd members and younger ones within a social group. This form of working together is completely different than merely pressing the right "buttons" to make him perform as you wish.

Furthermore, we must teach the horse in a logical manner using positive methods. Training techniques that are not horse friendly must be ruled out. Stress and pain do not create a positive connection between the horse's response and the "cause" of the response. They don't lead to building a positive relationship with the horse. As trainers and riders, we should consider ourselves a kind of "reward" for the horse, and he should come to feel good when he is praised for doing something well for us.

Often we have to get the horse accustomed to handling stressful situations without giving in to his flight instinct—for example, when being loaded in a strange horse trailer or when being mounted as a tractor drives by. Both are scenarios where it is important to wait until the horse has relaxed and noticed that he didn't "die" from the

Young horses often learn best and can accomplish new things most easily in a group.

threat because he stayed with the human rather than tried to flee. In other words, he survived the tractor experience with his human partner by his side. His recognition of surviving with his partner strengthens the relationship while at the same time creating pleasant associations associated with "staying" and helping to overcome his instinct to always run from perceived danger.

Trusting in us and feeling connected to us help the horse to withstand stress in any number of situations, enabling him to relax, think, and behave consciously. This is exactly what he experiences in the herd when he relies on the herd leader or leaders. (With this in mind, it is logical to take older, trustworthy horses that are high in the herd pecking order along with young horses on the first ride out or the first trip in the trailer. Horses in the herd learn like elephants— from the older ones.)

You can't ask a horse to "do nothing"

We must clearly understand that it is not possible to ask a horse to literally "do nothing" (that is, not react). As soon as we give an instruction to the horse, a movement impulse, than that leads to a reaction. But, while we can't say, "Do nothing," we can say, "Pay attention to me," "Concentrate on me," and "Wait for my next instruction." In effect this enables us to ask the horse to remain standing still, but to be actively alert. "Do nothing," is replaced with, "Please pay attention." Standing still under the rider is an especially good indicator for the quality of the relationship between the rider and horse. The rider needs to develop the ability to relax the horse. She needs to maintain concentration so that the horse stands still and immediately relaxes even after the intensity of a dressage exercise.

It is more difficult for untrained or poorly trained back muscles to cope with the rider's weight while the horse is standing still. It is

Use a mounting block when getting on out of respect for the horse's physical well-being. When mounting from the ground, the movement of the saddle presses on nerve endings in the withers area, causing the back musculature to tighten.

easier for him to bear and balance the weight in motion. Therefore, how the horse behaves when halting or when mounted tells us a lot about how the horse is being trained and about his physical progress.

Motivating the horse

When teaching the horse how to move in a way that is correct for his body and for dressage, we can use the fact that the horse figures out very quickly what movements in his repertoire are or aren't useful to him in a certain situation. However, training the horse in a conscientious manner and in a way that is best for him as a "horse" is not possible when we rely solely on the physical—that is, teaching him movements and improving his condition. We need to look "inside" him: Where does the horse get the motivation to participate in this difficult process for which he (most likely!) did not volunteer? Why should he willingly submit to mentally stressful physical exertion that is beyond what a flight animal can do in his natural balance?

The motivation the horse needs to actively participate as a "dance partner" can only come from two sources:

Jumping gymnastics on the longe line help the horse learn to take a jump out of a turn in the right tempo. In addition, his back bascule and upper neck musculature are strengthened; the horse becomes more elastic and develops more power.

- Trust in his training partner, the human. This is gained when we never disappoint him, and when we show him that we understand him, care about him, and won't ask him to do the impossible.
- Training that provides him "movement challenges" and that make emotional and social sense to him. No horse is so "dumb" as to not notice when what we're asking makes no sense.

Training exercises should, therefore, be offered as "challenges" for horse and rider to meet together; they are neither "bad things" for the horse to "survive" nor should they be punishment for his poor performance. Remember, every time the horse and rider solve a problem together, their relationship strengthens and the horse's confidence increases.

Although we should generally avoid anthropomorphizing, it does seem that, when it comes to sport, the mind-body connection functions similarly in human and horse. Therefore, in training the horse we can heed the saying, "Treat your horse as you'd like to be treated." Or, another way to look at it is to know that what helps or hurts us in accomplishing a difficult mind-body task, also either helps or hurts the horse.

The Rider's Responsibility to the Horse

According to classical philosophy, we as riders have a great responsibility to our horse: namely, the duty to work on our seat, to critically examine our attitude toward the horse and riding in general, and to develop our riding feel. We must train body and mind to develop the necessary postures for riding (which we don't need in "regular" life), work on our symmetry, and nurture our own ability to go back and forth between firmness and relaxation if we want to engage with our horse.

When working over cavalletti at the trot, the horse should be supported by the trainer, who should ask for a tempo appropriate for him and his level of training, and adjust the side reins long enough that he is able to use his neck for balance if necessary. In this way, trainer and horse work together and the horse learns to form a movement plan.

We must school and develop our body awareness since generally we don't have it naturally. Many of my riding students notice after a few lessons that they are using muscles that they didn't even know they had (never mind being able to use those muscles independently). These muscles are primarily in the stomach, back, hips, and thighs. Those who take up yoga, ballet, or belly dancing have a similar experience after the first few classes.

Only in therapeutic riding is the complete relaxation of the rider logical. Riding in all other scenarios requires a state of firmness in the rider's body.

A good rider should recognize and be able to feel when she is hindering the horse's flow of motion and be able to adjust as necessary. Yielding is the magic word here: she must loosen her body's tension and replace it with subtle movements that support the horse in his work. You can be sure that 99 percent of the "negative" tension in a horse is caused by the rider and therefore must be fixed on the rider's end.

The rider as the leading dance partner

As we've discussed, the human has less body awareness and power than the horse, but we also know the human has more logical intelligence and knowledge about biomechanics, training techniques, and psychology. The human in the horse-and-rider partnership has, therefore, the leading role in the "dance" and the responsibility for the overall performance. As the leading dance partner, the rider is obliged to explain to the horse—in a way he understands—what he needs to do so that they can move better together. And the rider should be able to motivate the horse to want to do it.

The rider should be able to motivate her horse even though it probably never crossed his mind to run around in circles with a heavy backpack on his back! Since the rider is the "backpack," it is of the utmost importance to make the horse's job easier instead of more difficult, and this requires a lot of physical ability, which the rider must develop.

When we train our own horse, acting as both athlete and coach, we frequently stumble against our own limits, as well as those of our horse. The better we get, the more we realize that there is much more to learn and practice in order to achieve the dream of "becoming one"—to move with him in harmony, supple but powerful. We yearn

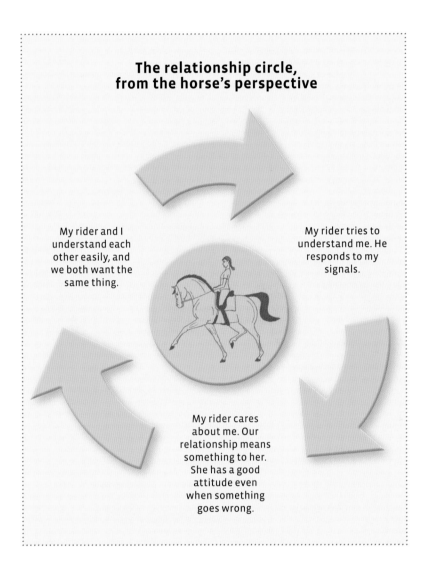

**The relationship circle,
from the horse's perspective**

My rider and I understand each other easily, and we both want the same thing.

My rider tries to understand me. He responds to my signals.

My rider cares about me. Our relationship means something to her. She has a good attitude even when something goes wrong.

for that happy feeling of harmony in movement, and we desire it more frequently and for longer periods of time.

How the Dialogue in Motion Works

The Horse's "Movement Plan"

We have already discussed how the dressage horse must develop a new body awareness in the course of his training. In order to coordinate his movements with a rider on his back, he also must learn, practice, and creatively employ new ways of "planning" his movement.

To enable the horse to do this, we must give him the chance to coordinate new movements without stress. He must be allowed to execute a "movement plan" without being disturbed by his rider. Unfortunately, reactive movement is more frequently seen in riding than consciously planned movement. These two types of movement differ in essential characteristics and affect how the horse experiences being ridden.

Planned movement versus reactive movement

Movement can occur in two fundamental ways:

- It can be planned in advance, controlled by the central nervous system, and translated as appropriate to the situation by the other senses.
- It can be reactive. The movement occurs as an automatic response to a stimulus with the other senses "turned off."

Even when it looks to us like the horse is performing the same movement from Point A to Point B, there can be different thought processes involved with different effects on biomechanics. This goes for the human, too. And since the horse must accommodate the weight of the rider, planned movement is undoubtedly preferable to reactive.

Disadvantages to reactive movement

Imagine that you are going for a long hike with a guide. You are crossing over a bridge that spans a dried-out, rocky creek bed. Suddenly, there's a rock slide from above, causing the guide to yell in warning and push you off the bridge to avoid being struck, and you end up in the creek bed.

The likelihood of you being injured or at the least landing hard on the rocky creek bed floor is much greater than if you had consciously decided to jump from the bridge yourself. In the latter case you would

Reactive, Conscious, or Planned Movement

We can identify three stages of movement development:
1) Reactive
2) Conscious
3) Planned

A simple exercise can explain the difference between reactive and conscious movement. Sit straight on a chair and simply let your head fall forward (from the position shown in 1 to the position in 2). Then, repeat the exercise, but this time, move your head consciously from Position 1 to Position 2. Repeat the two movements again and notice the distinct differences. Simply letting your head "fall forward" generally doesn't feel pleasant, especially where the muscles and connective tissue attach to the bones. In comparison, conscious movement of the head from Position 1 to Position 2 ensures that the head sinks slowly and in a controlled manner that shouldn't feel unpleasant.

Moving in a planned way is the next and more advanced step of conscious movement: a single movement is or combination of movements are planned ahead of time and then consciously executed. Try this exercise as an example (see photos 3–5): While standing and looking ahead of you, visualize stretching your right arm straight out in front of you, moving more slowly as the arm reaches shoulder height. Then, close your eyes and do the movement as planned. Most people don't get the planned movement exactly right the first time. After a few repetitions of the same movement plan, they have it down

1 - 4 *Another exercise to notice the difference between reactive and planned movement: have an assistant tap your knee with a mallet (reactive), then consciously plan to lift the leg out straight before you, close your eyes, and intentionally move the limb from Point A to Point B (planned).*

have been able to first evaluate how high and far to jump, you could have looked for a good place to land, and then you could have propelled yourself from the bridge accordingly. During the jump you could have brought your hips, knees, and ankles under your center of gravity, enabling you to land in the creek bed more softly with some shock absorption.

Consciously planned movement is very important in coordinated activities, as it considers all the joints, tendons, ligaments, and muscles in the movement plan. It allows there to be fluid motion without damaging jolts to the body.

When we are forced to move reactively, careful coordination is not possible. We are more likely to be clumsy because we don't have time to consider the required movement sequence through our "central planning station," aka the brain. The result is little if any shock ab-

"Throwing" the legs high in the dressage arena is often reactive movement due to stress; it may look spectacular but it stresses the joints.

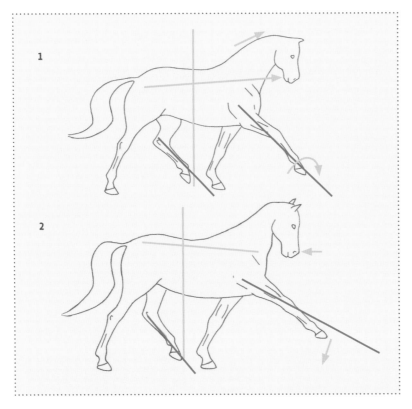

1 *When the horse moves with a plan, his movements are fluid, the forward and backward striding legs are parallel, and the horse steps well under his center of gravity.*

2 *The effect of reactive movement, often due to stress: a stiff back, stamping movement, and the horse doesn't sufficiently step under his center of gravity.*

sorption in our movement, which causes stress on or injury to the movement apparatus (made up of muscles, tendons, ligaments, joints).

When under stress, both human and horse move mostly reactively: responses to stress happen fast, with only a moment of thought, and without careful coordination of the movement apparatus.

Supporting or limiting the "movement plan"

Riding in a way that is correct and best for the horse requires that we give the horse the chance to plan his coordinated movement, without stress, even with a rider on his back.

Unfortunately, the horse's ability to actively plan his movement can be hindered or completely blocked by the rider in several ways:

1 When she forces him into positions that make it impossible for him to find or reestablish his balance.

2 When she causes him pain.
3 When she causes his muscles to tighten or to remain in a stressed
   state of tension so that he fatigues quickly.

   These mistakes are usually not intentional on the part of the
rider but are the result of insufficient ability or a lack of knowledge.
However, there is also a trend in riding that intentionally replaces
the horse's ability to consciously plan his movement with reactive
movement. Most riders don't sufficiently appreciate how unpleasant
this is for the horse and injure him in the long-term. In the pages
ahead, we will focus on the phenomenon of "learned helplessness"
that is characteristic of many top dressage athletes who subscribe to
these techniques.

The challenge of visual orientation

In accepting his role under saddle, the dressage horse must adjust to
yet another aspect of the mind-body relationship. He must learn to
de-emphasize (to a certain degree) his own visual orientation (visual

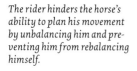

*The rider hinders the horse's
ability to plan his movement
by unbalancing him and preventing him from rebalancing
himself.*

1

2

feedback from landmarks to help in mobility and direction) in creating a movement plan, and learn instead to trust more in the plan of the rider. This can be a bit of a struggle for him initially. We can view this phenomenon when the horse travels on a circle on the longe line and when he is ridden on the second or third track (off the rail) under saddle.

When longed in the middle of an arena, the horse is drawn to the track at the fence line on two sides of the circle: instead of a round circle, he makes an oval. When he is ridden on the second or third track, he is again drawn to the visual boundary along the rail. Even well-trained and well-ridden horses exhibit this phenomenon when the trainer or rider doesn't support the horse enough in his movement plan, or if the horse isn't appropriately straight on curved lines and when ridden in varying degrees of collection.

Since the horse is narrower at the shoulders than at the hindquarters, he is naturally crooked if we let him follow his urge to gravitate toward walls, fences, or visual lines. This is why we should dispense with exercises, as soon as is possible, that encourage crookedness due to primary visual orientation—for example, the leg yield on the wall.

1–2 When halting the horse, the rider can support his movement plan with her correct application of her seat, legs, and hands (1). When the rider applies these aids in an overly intense manner, the horse stops reactively, with a stiff, blocked back, to the pull on the reins. He is unable to benefit from the natural spring action of the hindquarters (hips, stifles, and hocks) that can protect the forehand and the back from strain and injury (2).

1

2

1 *A straight horse traverses a corner.*

2 *A twist of the neck or tilt of the head indicates a lack of straightness.*

For the same reason, longeing or doing a lot of groundwork in a round pen is not logical. It isn't just that the horse doesn't want to go straight because he is visually attached to the fence line; work in a round pen or circular ring doesn't help the horse progress in terms of his ability to form and adhere to a movement plan. It doesn't pre-pare him for the new movement patterns needed to move correctly on curved lines. The horse isn't encouraged to step diagonally under his center of gravity with the inside hind leg, nor is he helped to straighten his forehand in front of his hindquarters. Instead, his inclination for crookedness, heaviness on the forehand, and visual orientation is reinforced.

The same problems arise in different forms of liberty work, groundwork, and other techniques common to our diverse modern methods. This isn't to say that you shouldn't let your horse run free sometimes and play a little. But that has nothing to do with training or work in the sense of improving the horse's coordinated physical development. And I have noticed that my horses get bored very quickly with such things.

Like humans, horses can't forget what they have learned before; they can only learn "over" it. Consequently, we should avoid anything that either gets in the way of the horse learning correct control of his movement or that strengthens incorrect movement habits.

Working with—not against—the horse

As we are beginning to see, for horse-and-rider partners to achieve movement goals together, they must both participate in the planning

1–2 When the rider rides a turn by pulling the horse's nose and neck too far to the inside (of the arena), the horse escapes through the outside shoulder.

1

2

1 *A horse that isn't yet well-trained and isn't ridden with enough support from the rider will orient himself visually to the outside track, drift toward the rail, and get crooked.*

2 *When traveling on a circle, whether longed or ridden, the horse is pulled visually in the direction of the fence or wall.*

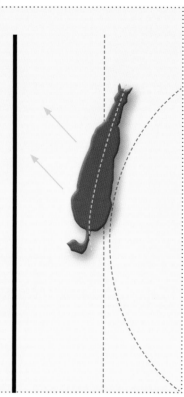

and execution of the individual parts that make up the whole. The rider must strive to apply her aids at the correct time to give the horse the possibility of integrating her directions into his movement plan.

To this end, the human must develop a correct seat that is consistently balanced over the horse's center of gravity. Her aids should not inhibit or disrupt the horse, forcing him to react reflexively. They should allow the horse time to plan his movements himself.

Although we humans tend to be first-class "control freaks," we should at least give the horse control over his own movement plan, since as the leading dance partner, we already define his direction, tempo, and gait. Otherwise, we demotivate and discourage him from solving movement challenges with us. As riders, we should focus our need to control something on our own body awareness and aids so we can improve them in ways that benefit of the horse.

Types of "Riding Dialogue"

How we talk with other humans says a lot about our relationship with them. The same goes for horses: we can treat our horse as a partner with whom we accomplish something or with whom we simply have fun; or, we can treat him as a subject who must obey and carry out orders (that often make no sense to him).

Since horses can't speak as we do, riders must communicate with their mount in another way. The "language" that we choose—meaning the training method and the riding style—shape the relationship between our dissimilar beings. There are huge differences between various forms of dialogue, which I describe below. A good observer—a judge at a competition for example—should be able to recognize how well rider and horse understand one another via their dialogue.

The military dialogue: There is no actual conversation here. The one giving the order (the rider) is not interested in receiving an answer from the one receiving the order (the horse). He should simply obey without question. Orders should be carried out reflexively. Horses

1 *There is no dialogue here: the horse is receiving an order, and the rider is not interested in an answer, only obedience.*

2 *The military dialogue.*

The business dialogue.

The partnership dialogue.

that submit to the will of their rider in this dialogue are dull and resigned.

The business dialogue: In this form of dialogue, two partners who aren't necessarily of the same level or rank, work together and interact with one another. It is expected that both partners participate in the dialogue, and both think before they reply to the other. This form of dialogue is easy to imagine in horse training. The rider considers the reactions ("replies") of the horse and builds the training session on them.

The friendship dialogue: Here both the rider and horse's feelings and the relationship they have play a stronger role than in the strictly "business" model. Ideally, riders and horses should be friends and "partners" in what they do together.

The relationship dialogue.

The relationship dialogue: Emotions play a still greater role here than they do in the business or friendship dialogue. Such an intimate dialogue between human and horse is more likely from the ground than from the saddle. The danger in this dialogue is that the human will anthropomorphize the horse and have "romantic" expectations that the horse can't possibly fulfill.

The therapeutic dialogue: Here, rider and horse have different roles—that of therapist and client. Emotions and thinking play a large part. The therapist leads the process, and the client determines the topic, speed, progress, and the depth of the process. This is the classical interaction when a horse with behavioral or training problems is in retraining. Maybe the horse is helped to trust humans again after a bad experience, or perhaps he's being rehabilitated after a physical injury. In either case, empathy on the therapist's part is an important factor.

The therapeutic dialogue.

Dialogue Exercise for Riders

In a conversation, it is not just what is said that is important, but also how it is said, including the attitude one assumes when delivering a message and the overall atmosphere surrounding the conversation.

This simple exercise, which you can do with a friend, can clarify the different attitudes and atmospheres that can play a role in riding dialogues:

Standing side by side, press one hand against one of your friend's hands. Determine which one of you will be the "leader" first. If you are to lead her first, do so using only the movement signals you can give using the palm of your hand. When you provide signals in a respectful and courteous way, your friend will understand what you want more quickly and move as indicated more readily. When your attitude is disrespectful and demanding, your friend's body and mind will react to the rude request by stiffening and "blocking." When you, the leading dance partner, are hesitant or you aren't concentrating on the directions you are giving, your friend will become uncomfortable, insecure, and will just do what you "hope" is correct. Lack of concentration on the part of the leader feels like disrespect to your partner.

1-4 *This simple exercise with a partner shows you how your conversation with your horse will differ depending on your attitude when giving the aids.*

Coordinating the Primary Aids

According to classical training, the primary rider aids are those that support the horse's movement plan. The rider has three types of aids available: the seat, the legs, and the rein aids. Each dressage movement is ridden with the aids applied at varying levels of intensity and in different combinations.

Let's look at the half-halt as an example of how integral the combination of aids can be: without the use of the seat and leg aids, which assure that the amplitude of movement isn't interrupted, the horse's hind end shuts down, the horse bumps against the bit, and the exercise degenerates into merely pulling on the reins.

The rider's every body part has its own job. The torso should disturb the horse as little as possible. It should remain very quiet and stabile over the horse's center of gravity so the horse doesn't have to keep readjusting his balance in an attempt to stay in sync with his rider.

The "core" of the rider (stomach, lower back, pelvis, seat bones, and hips) is the important center of communication between her and her horse. The rider should give signals for specific movements through her seat, while her legs and hands play a smaller role. The rider's core directly influences the ability of the horse's back to "swing" and the connectivity between the front and hind ends. She wants the horse to be able to "go and get" the hindquarters in response to certain signals at the center of his body. Through her core, the rider can stimulate the relaxed and swinging back muscles to move with greater or lesser amplitude—for example, as is necessary in a lengthening or shortening of the trot.

The rider's legs have a number of functions. When applied on one side, the leg can stimulate the horse's hind leg on the same side to step farther under the horse's body. The legs can give lateral signals and help the horse bend on curves.

The rider's hands assure that the horse moves in a certain frame: forward-downward or, according to his ability, more or less collected and upright. The hands coordinate with the rest of the aids so that the horse is properly flexed (or when wrongly applied, overflexed) in the neck, and the nose is in front of or on (or again, incorrectly behind)

Different parts of the rider's body influence different regions of the horse's body in the dialogue of motion dialogue.

the vertical. When successfully coordinated with the seat and the legs, the hands encourage the horse to stretch to the bit and practically become part of the horse's body. As mentioned, the hands can also negatively affect the mouth and disturb the horse's flow of movement, interrupting the dialogue of motion.

When the hands work in sync with the other aids or impulses, and react to what the horse "replies," then the horse's movements are not interrupted because the hands are merely helping the horse increase or decrease the scope of his movement and adjust his frame accordingly.

This rider and the horse are having a conversation: the rider needs to listen to her horse's "reply," taking the hint from his switching tail and giving with her inside hand.

The horse must have the chance to incorporate the movement requests of the rider into his movement plan in accordance with his condition, level of training, and his current state of mind. This means that he might indicate that a movement isn't possible just now.

When this is the case, the rider must look for possible causes and work with the horse to get through them. Usually, these are rider errors or problems in the human-horse relationship; however, other possible causes include physical problems in the horse, training that is progressing too rapidly, or fatigue. In the classical way of thinking, resistances are symptoms of problems. And these problems cannot be fixed by simply applying more pressure, being more controlling, or employing auxiliary equipment.

1 *When signals for movement are given respectfully with rider and horse in sync and in harmony, a pleasant, fluid motion is the result*

2 *Uncoordinated signals and forceful pressure cause counter-pressure and interrupt the flow of movement between partners.*

Pressure causes counter-pressure

Some current riding trends teach that when a horse doesn't respond to an aid, the aid must be given again more forcefully. A simple exercise with a friend shows that this usually only leads to stiffening and leaning in the horse, not to the development of fluid motion. Position yourself behind your partner with your hands on her waist. Both of you start jogging slowly forward. Using pressure from one hand, try to move your friend in a different direction, off your current path of travel. Increase the pressure, putting all your power behind the effort. Your partner will stiffen in response, and although you might get her to move in the direction of your choosing, she will only go with evident resistance rather than freely swinging and planned movement. Your friend, your "horse," can't help but reactively "block" the push from your hand. Simply said, pressure usually creates counter-pressure.

1

2

Aligning the horse's natural impulse with the rider's aids

When using the primary aids, the horse's natural impulse "to do something" is replaced by a signal from the rider. When applied with empathy, the aids are the equivalent of the horse deciding for himself that he would like to canter, and then doing it.

As we have already seen, for a movement to be successful, the horse must be appropriately motivated to participate, in a positive and relaxed frame, and engaged in an active and concentrated conver-

Here horse and rider are engaged in a dialogue as they concentrate on a movement: the leg-yield.

sation. The rider can then present her movement request in a way that "awakens" the impulse in the horse to want to do it. This requires "fingertip feel" and technical precision.

To understand this better, let's consider a horse picking up the canter of his own free will when loose in the pasture as compared to cantering at the rider's request.

When a horse is loose in the pasture, an external signal, such as the cantering of other horses, causes him to want to canter, as well. He organizes his body in the necessary position, starts cantering, and continues cantering until he notices that he is nearing the fence line at the end of the pasture or that he is a little tired and wants to trot.

When a horse is under saddle, the movement goes this way: The rider decides to start cantering. She tries to engender in the horse the same feeling he would experience naturally if he decided to canter off when loose in the pasture. She does this so he can make a movement plan. She shares her intentions with the horse through her seat, which she uses to say: "Let's get more active, okay?" This is the first indication of "something to come" for the horse. If horse and rider are in sync and balanced in harmonious movement, the horse will accept the rider's suggestion of activity and be tuned in and ready for something new. It is then relatively easy to get him to start cantering. The horse is mentally and physically ready to canter, and the rider can feel that he is in the "start position." By the time the rider gives the final aid for canter, the horse does it out of his own impulse. He has had time to begin to want to canter, and had just been waiting for the signal from the rider to begin.

The half-halt as a preparatory signal

Riders who have trained a horse according to classical principles don't appear to give visible aids; the horse seems to respond to the rider's thoughts. This results from the rider and the horse actually being in a constant dialogue of motion and aids. Throughout, half-halts play the role of preparatory signal.

Unfortunately it is a widespread misunderstanding that you only need to tug on the reins to prepare the horse for something new. A half-halt is actually a much more complex thing than a mere pull on the reins. The half-halt enables the rider to bring the horse into balance and put him into a "start position" for the next movement. The horse notices this and thinks, "Ah! Something is about to happen. My rider wants to do something different." He prepares himself mentally for a new movement suggestion from the rider, and if the rider doesn't disrupt him but gives him the opportunity to get into the biomechanically correct position necessary to, for example, start cantering, then the horse can comfortably and willingly respond to the aids. In our example of picking up the canter, these are specifically:

- The inside leg at the girth, bending the horse.
- The outside leg (outside the bend) behind the girth, asking the hindquarters to be more active.
- The inside hand, "giving" forward.
- The outside hand, inviting the horse to stretch into the outside rein.
- The rider's core, maintaining the swing of the horse's back and giving the signal to change gait.

When something goes wrong with the canter transition, it is usually due to the rider: poor preparation, bad timing, or lack of balance. On the other hand, with an active dialogue of motion the canter depart is fluid.

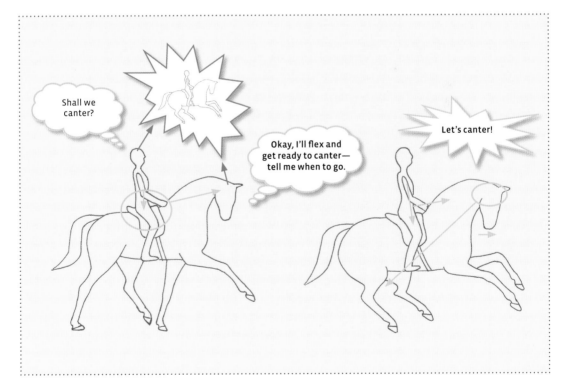

Horses can easily figure out the communication "code" provided by the primary aids (see p. 59).

A natural code of communication

Communication through the primary aids has nothing to do with push-button obedience or a military dialogue (see p. 55). The rider must be consistently and constantly alert to how she should seek to get what she wants from the horse. When the horse isn't well enough prepared for a movement—when asked to canter, he starts trotting faster, for example—the rider's preparation must be corrected before the dialogue can continue. Sometimes the rider isn't quite with the movement or her timing isn't right, as I've mentioned.

Whether the rider-and-horse dialogue is as between business colleagues or friends, or as in a relationship (see p. 56-57), good communication is a question of the two personalities interacting and using the "code" of the primary aids. This code (the interplay of fine movement impulses) was very carefully determined by the classical masters who worked with young, green, and experienced horses that had been ridden for years under pressure to figure out how they would react to the primary aids. The classical masters developed the primary aids from first observing the nature of the horse, considering their physical and anatomical perspectives, testing them, and finally codifying them. The result is that we don't need to put a lot of effort into teaching the horse the meanings of the aids. I am always astonished how fast young horses react to them.

Secondary aids work as disruptions

The difference between classical dressage training and the forms of training that have been gaining ground on the international dressage scene over the last few years, touches on the art of communicating with the horse.

In classical training, the dance partners (horse and rider) communicate as we have discussed, notably through intuitively understandable movement impulses, each "opening" him- or herself to receive information from his or her partner and reply to it.

The principle is different with many "modern" training methods where the horse is "programmed" to react a certain way. He learns to respond with certain movements to certain stimuli or "secondary aids," which do not make sense to him. This methodology is driven by the human need to control while sparing the rider the intensive schooling required to develop an effective seat and understanding of the primary aids. The rider doesn't have to think about the individual horse, his patterns and characteristics of movement, because every horse is required to react to a "push of a button."

In a classical dialogue of motion, the horse is allowed to think alongside the rider, to make suggestions and give vetoes. Here Ravenna collects herself so much that it becomes a levade; her rider accepts this offered answer, although it isn't what she had planned.

Here the horse is degraded and commanded to obey the orders he receives. His physical expression shows that he doesn't enjoy the experience.

This type of riding reduces the horse's independence in forming a movement plan and creates stress. The rider uses signals that don't have anything to do with the primary aids. These "secondary aids" usually disrupt the fluidity of movement and undermine the well-being of the horse. The horse must react as the rider commands. There is no consideration of the horse's response in this process—it is less about communication between partners and more about the rider asking questions that he expects the horse to answer correctly and immediately. While this description may make it seem harmless enough, the attitude of the rider in the dialogue lacks respect for the horse. It is all "stimulus-response" and riding with obvious secondary aids, to which the horse reacts reflexively.

The Independent Seat as the Key to the Dialogue of Motion

Riding's dialogue of motion stems from body language between both partners. The "vocabulary" includes the aids and the independent seat of the rider. It is actually misleading in some ways to talk about the "seat," since it implies "sitting," which suggests that the rider rests passively on the horse and is carried around. This isn't what happens in a dialogue of motion—rather, the rider is engaged in a continuous sending and receiving of movement impulses in order to communicate with the horse.

"Aids" are meant to "help"
Giving aids—as in helping the horse—requires the rider doesn't disturb the horse with her weight or her movements. She should also avoid stressing her own vertebral column.

This is accomplished with the classical independent seat, which isn't easy to achieve. Centuries have gone into figuring it out as a means of combining and melding rider and horse into one: a single entity, swinging with amplitude, moving beautifully and efficiently, without potential injury to either partner.

Every biomechanical detail is important to an independent seat. The smallest deviations are disturbing to the horse. But an indepen-

You must continually work on establishing and maintaining an independent seat. The smallest details are important.

dent seat also involves a mental requirement: that of desiring the horse to enjoy participating in the work we do together. We can optimally support the horse with our seat, but we can also bother him, and cause him stress and frustration. If we love our horse and want to help him to enjoy dressage, we must be ready to invest a lot in our seat.

From a mind-body perspective, the rider must incorporate a lot of factors into her seat that are important to the dialogue of motion. She must:

A lesson focused on developing mind-body awareness on the longe line is an excellent way to develop the rider's seat and feel.

- Feel not only what the horse does, but also what he is thinking about doing and what he is offering to do.

- Communicate to the horse her own motivation and preparation for the training session.
- Be physically "open" to the horse, just as the horse is "open" to the rider through his relaxed and swinging back—in other words, throughness.

The rider must be able to exhibit what we refer to as throughness in the horse if she wishes to have a physical and mental dialogue with him. The rider can only expect throughness from her horse when she herself is through in her seat. This means being open to a continuous exchange of contact and information, passed from her to the horse via her seat and reins, and from the horse back to her.

Development of rider feel

It is just as important for the rider to develop feel as it is for her to learn the technical side of an independent seat and how to give the aids. She must be in tune to the feeling of moving together with the horse, and the flow of motion and body communication they experience. It means being open to the signals that the horse is continuously sending her. In addition, the rider must develop a good feel for her

Beginner dressage riders should learn the dialogue of motion with the help of a good instructor and develop an independent seat on an experienced horse that has been classically trained.

own body. Finally, she should be able to incorporate all of this in a dialogue of motion with the horse.

When learning movements with developing feel in mind, it is important ask ourselves the following questions:

· How am I moving myself, and how am I being moved by the horse?
· How is the movement going for me—that is, how does it feel?
· How am I reacting (in body and mind) to this movement?
· What makes me afraid or causes me to stiffen?
· What causes me to react in this way to the horse, and how does he react in response?

It is very important for the rider to consciously grasp what riding is in this phase. Performing exercises on the longe line with only a surcingle (outfitted for vaulting or therapy) allows the rider to be in very direct connection with the horse and promote awareness of her body and her horse's. The rider can learn to enjoy the movement of the horse in different positions (in addition to the standard "astride") before she begins to actively ride and guide the horse. Such movement exercises prepare her well for developing a healthy dialogue in the course of training her horse later.

1-2 *Working on the seat while on the longe line should accomplish more than the ability to physically move with the horse. Such exercises can also develop a rider's ability to perceive movement and thus improve feel. It is necessary to use a horse that is completely relaxed and that can be involved in a dialogue of motion with the rider. This ensures the rider can experience how the horse reacts to her movement impulses and her periods of relaxation.*

1

2

3

"Feel" can't be learned purely mechanically, so it isn't logical to try to teach someone to ride on a movement simulator. From the moment we get on a horse, the horse reacts to us just as we react to him. A simulator doesn't accurately reflect that. There is a simulator in the horse museum in Münster, Germany, that is very nice for demonstrating three-dimensionally the walk, trot, and canter; however, it doesn't teach a person how to really ride.

Lessons that use only a surcingle (no saddle) and ask the rider to sit in different positions benefit the development of the rider's seat. They also encourage a dialogue of motion partly because the rider can't think of using any "secondary aids" since she is riding with neither reins nor saddle—instead, she can develop rider feel.

Rider coordination and symmetry

Naturally, you can't gain a good classical seat and the ability to communicate tactfully with the horse in a single day. Riding well requires dedication to a long and difficult mind-body learning process, which is not dissimilar to what the horse experiences as he is educated as a dressage horse.

We must recognize that riding is a sport, and as in other sports, coordination is critical. It shows a significant overestimation of our abilities when we think we can easily achieve the kind of skill in the saddle that ballet dancers train five to six hours a day for years to acquire. They spend hours in front of the mirror, working to develop fine muscle control and symmetrical movement.

1-2 *The rider can work on improving her body symmetry and coordination on the horse, as well as off the horse, spending time on training muscle control and movement, like a ballet dancer does.*

And there are other similarities to sports, which should be considered. For example, in order to be able to ride well, we should be able to write right-handed or left handed—how can we support the horse in becoming straight if we can't be straight and symmetrical in our own body? And it is at the very least impolite to our athletic partner, the horse, to get on his back and start riding without warming up our body. We would never think of doing such a thing in other sports.

As we have already discussed in this book, body awareness and off-horse physical training are as important as actually riding to gain the ability to control your body in the saddle.

Just as the horse must be loosened and warmed up prior to the start of a training session, so should the rider before she gets on.

The Principles of the Dialogue of Motion

The fundamental mind-body principles of the dialogue of motion are implicitly incorporated in the classical dressage teachings, though not with any such terminology or labels attached. Therefore, I have given these principles names that have helped my students understand them.

The arch principle

As horizontally oriented beings, horses lift their back when ridden correctly, and it is the curve of the arched back that lets us sit comfortably. As vertically moving beings, we humans must arch forward our chest-stomach-hip regions. The arch in horse and rider allows more to be accomplished with less (unnecessary and perhaps disruptive) movement. When horse and rider succeed in "tuning" their respective arch in to the other's, little movements can have a large effect.

The finely tuned arches of horse and rider.

The rider can only invite the horse to participate in a pleasant contact when she can carry her hands independently from the rest of her body.

The independence principle

The rider must be able to move all her body parts and muscles independently from one another, without losing balance, blocking the dialogue of motion, or disturbing the horse's movement. Many body movements are naturally connected in our coordination system. We have to learn to first separate them in order to be able to intentionally employ them as individual elements. In addition, we must be able to tighten and relax specific areas of the body, either simultaneously or sequentially.

Appropriate exercises on the longe line can help riders learn how to do this, but there are also some that can be practiced in everyday life. The development of the rider's independent coordination is comparable to the regular daily exercises required of a ballet dancer.

The scales principle

This principle is seen most clearly in the "relative elevation" that is characteristic of collection—the horse is beyond his natural horizontal balance and in an uphill balance, with his hindquarters a little lower and deeper (further beneath the horse's torso) than the forehand, as seen when one side of a pair of scales is weighted.

The scales principle begins with engaged, forward-downward riding while stretching, and it ends with the levade. The scales are weighted by little more than a half-halt. The rider "holds" the horse with her seat and under her weight, the "rear scale" (hindquarters) automatically stays down while the "front scale" (forehand) lifts a little without the horse having to push harder off the ground with his front legs.

The balance principle

The horse can only balance the rider while staying true to his path of travel when the rider sits vertically in the saddle. If the rider cocks one hip or pulls one leg up, then the horse must step under the displaced weight. On a volte the horse will drift in, while on a straight line, he will have to change direction.

The horse doesn't naturally turn making good use of his hind end as we want him to in a change of direction. His weight tends to fall on the forehand. This causes many riders to ride turns using undesirable

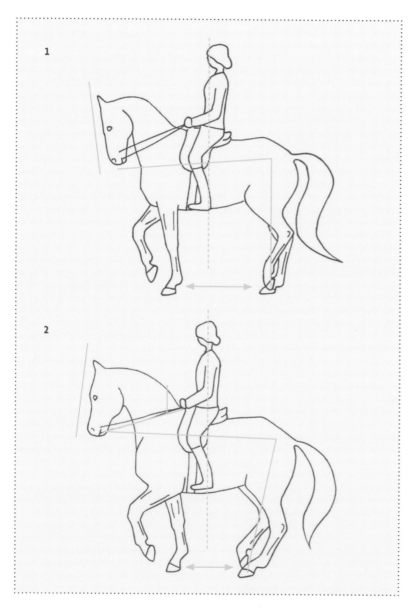

1 When the horse is "blocked" in front and the rider doesn't sit straight, neither the scales principle nor the balance principle can come into effect.

2 Here the scales principle and the balance principle are fulfilled: the horse is in "self-carriage," stepping under his center of gravity (note the "rear scale's" position, lower and deeper than the "front scale."

"secondary aids" (see p. 64), sometimes without even knowing it. Here again, lessons on the longe line can be of benefit as the horse teaches us to feel his movement on the turn, and the rider learns to correct herself in response to the the horse.

The anticipation principle

The rider must look forward, think in advance, and give the horse enough time to incorporate her signals into his own movement plan. She must allow time for her movement impulses to be expressed through the horse's.

When the rider just "goes along" with the movement of the horse, we miss a certain dynamic. It isn't clear to the horse what should actually be happening and consequently he can't prepare himself properly. When the rider thinks far enough ahead, her anticipation is translated through her body, and there is the feeling that she gives the horse a subtle suggestion, and then rider and horse complete the movement together.

1–2 The plug principle: the seat bones are like the two prongs of an electrical plug, through which the primary communicative information passes.

1

2

The plug principle

Our two seat bones are the two prongs of the "plug" of communication. Only when they are in direct contact with the horse can the most important connection occur. The seat bones can only stay in contact with the horse when the rider sits straight with her vertebral column in a natural, neutral, S-shape. A helpful image is to imagine the rider as Donald Duck, with his tail stuck out behind him. This position should not be confused with riding with a hollow back.

The lower back musculature must be well trained to be able to sit the canter (for example) while keeping the "plug" plugged in.

The dialogue principle

Horse and rider both have their part to play in their dialogue of motion. Both are involved in the decision regarding what will be done next. Horse and rider listen to each other and adjust to each other. Every new individual movement is the result of a conversation.

The concentration principle

Only when the rider fully concentrates on her horse and her task can she expect the same focus on her from her horse.

On the one hand, this principle is simply a matter of courtesy. On the other, the complex mind-body activity of riding can only be mastered when energy is not lost or wasted on other, unrelated tasks. This goes for both the rider and the horse. When one of the two is

See how this horse and rider are engaged in a conversation with full concentration on the movement task in the here-and-now.

distracted, the dialogue of motion suffers considerably. For example, shying horses are frequently the result of riders who aren't concentrating.

The "here-and-now" principle

When riding, the only thing that matters is the moment of moving together and what we want to achieve in that motion. Stresses, worries, and problems disturb this process and have no place in the saddle. Negative feelings and experiences should not be taken with us to the barn; they cause us to react unfairly to the horse, our partner.

Even when something goes wrong while riding, the rider shouldn't brood over it while in the saddle. That goes for during competition as well as in daily practice. You can think about what went awry later. The next movement, and your horse, deserve your full concentration.

Riding Well Means Having Ourselves Under Control

As a physical therapist, I know how difficult the mind-body learning process of riding is: overcoming our asymmetry (right- or left-hand-edness); recalibrating our body movement patterns; and learning how to "get in sync" with the movement of another being. It is easier to engage in a reasonable communication from the ground because we don't have to fear being run away with (for example) and little disturbs our body control.

Rider fear and a human need to dominate are involved when forceful auxiliary aids are used on the horse.

As riders we must learn to overcome our instinctive fear of our horse moving unexpectedly. It is hard for us to give up a certain level of control. We also have to understand our own psychology and learn

to control our emotions in order to be able to interpret and properly respond to a horse's wanted (or unwanted) reactions to the movement impulses we give.

We all know how much willpower it takes to "let go" and to relax when we are paralyzed with fear—and how easy it is to simply clutch at our horse when he is also reacting in fear. This fear can lead to us feeling a need to control the horse that shuts out any other possible understanding. We rely on domination rather than dialogue.

Learning to ride means to continually learn, over and over again, how to deal with frustration. The horse will always react to our inability to avoid disturbing his movements or any attempts to force him to do something he doesn't understand—and sometimes the reaction can be big.

It is frustration, and even hopelessness, that causes humans to search for techniques to make the problem of dealing with the horse's reactions easier to solve: the equestrian business is full of all kinds of reins, bits, and other complicated equipment. But there is no avoiding the fact that if we want to ride well, there is only one way to do it: work on our own mind-body ability (training our independent seat), as well as keeping our reactions to our horse's reactions under control.

Riding "free" from the confines of tack is fun for both horse and rider!

The most dangerous and painful aid in the drive for control and dominance is the human herself, who can abuse the horse with what would otherwise be perfectly reasonable equipment, such as the bit. Just as a scalpel in the hand of surgeon can be lifesaving while in the hand of a murderer deadly, the curb bit can become an instrument of torture in the hands of a rider who is anxious and seeking control.

Riders who are not ready to confront their own weaknesses and work on their ability and attitude often seek fads to spare themselves what is a difficult process. Certain trends come to mind here where instead of working on herself in order to develop better balance and hand coordination, the rider holds the reins too tight. Instead of practicing a dialogue of motion and the control of her fine motor skills, she limits herself to "stepping on the gas" and "braking." Still more simplifications of a complex dynamic actually serve to make this manner of riding attractive to many of those watching, and it grows more popular because it is easy to do. But this form of riding is absolutely not horse friendly.

Mind-Body Learning in the Training of Horse and Rider

The Phases of the Learning Process

What does the mind-body learning process look like when it involves a horse and rider who are learning new movements and integrating them into already familiar movement patterns?

The process for both builds in steps:

1 Learn the movement.

2 Practice it.

3 Train it.

During the learning process, horse and rider must be able to answer the questions that follow in theory and in practice. The horse learns through his trainer; the rider through her riding instructor. Let's look at the questions first from the rider's point of view:

Can I do it? The first thing to ask yourself is, "Am I currently able to perform the necessary physical movements?"

Since in the modern day we spend so much time sitting, we are much less flexible than we need to be to ride. Our muscles are not long enough (to be able to put our leg in the right spot, for example), and our feel is not yet developed for the many ways we can effectively use our core. We must learn to consciously move individual muscle groups and joints as required while riding.

It is important to have a mental picture of what good riding looks like. This is a lovely moment between horse and rider, although for safety reasons, a riding helmet should always be worn.

What does it look like? Many riders have no real picture of what good riding or harmonious motion of horse and rider looks like. The correct "visual" is necessary in order to be able to attain your riding goals. An image of the movement beautifully ridden can serve as an inner video of what it looks like when it is done well.

What do I have to do? You need to program your own body in order to be able to intentionally coordinate the movement when needed.

How does it feel when it is right? It takes a while until we can feel that a horse is going well under us. Especially when we are working on our own. For this reason, seat training on the longe line is essential

1 *Flexibility exercises can help you discover the ways your body can move.*

2 *That also goes for the horse.*

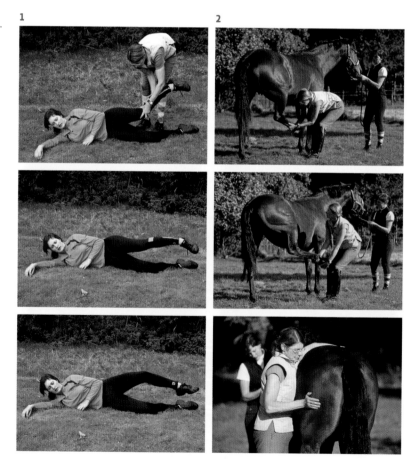

1   2

early in the development of every rider. The riding instructor can allow the horse to move around a circle, and the rider can experience how it feels to sit on a relaxed horse. Then she knows what she must develop from the saddle in a later phase of the learning process. There are unfortunately significant misunderstandings about what "good rider feel" is, and when a riding instructor doesn't specifically ask about it, it is hard to tell if the rider has saved the correct feeling in her own inner-movement-memory-bank so she can recall it at a moment's notice later on.

When the rider is conscious of how she is moving but doesn't have to think too much about it, she is in a position to improve how the horse is moving.

Can I do it without having to think about it? It is a big step forward in the learning process when certain movement combinations can be done almost automatically and without our full concentration. I remember my riding students saying things like, "When I don't watch my hand every minute, it goes up when I try to relax my thigh!" or "When I don't think constantly about 'making myself long' I collapse after only a few yards!"

It takes effort before a correctly learned movement pattern can be repeated without thinking about it. Riding is a multitasking business. Like a computer, different chains of events and processes must continue automatically in the background, but be consciously visible (on the screen) when necessary. Such processes are called preconscious.

Can I improve what I have already internalized? This question comes up when the rider has achieved the goal of performing without thinking about it. Through repetition, meaning practice, the quality of the movement pattern improves. It fits the horse and the situation better. The quality of the execution of the movement is improved.

Can I use what I have already learned to support and improve the horse in his movements? This question doesn't come up until the end of a long learning process. Only at this point is the rider in the position to work with the horse without disturbing him in his movement plan; to consciously help him; and to be better able to move with him.

This series of questions outlines the ideal learning process, and

1

2

1–2 Work on the wooden horse helps provide students body and movement awareness and the ability to self-evaluate movements in the saddle.

Movement exercises on an exercise ball can help the rider find the correct posture and balance of her seat in the saddle.

riders should follow it sequentially. I believe that many riders simply leave out some steps. This isn't actually so surprising since there are few riding instructors who offer lessons in good, correct mind-body training.

At the Spanish Riding School, in Vienna, Austria, students always take daily longe lessons that focus on developing the seat with gymnastic exercises. In the tradition of the Spanish Riding School, the rider program to which I subscribe corresponds precisely to the guidelines for good mind-body learning: the phases of learning movements go from "still not knowing or being able to" to "can do with concentration" and finally to "don't even have to think about it"—the automatic execution of the necessary movements in riding. Throughout this process the rider must acquire and practice the basics:

1 Form an image of the movement.
2 Learn coordination of the movement.
3 Develop feel for the movement.
4 Explore the potential of the movement.

The horse goes through the same process as he learns to be ridden.

Should "students" be training "students"?

It is obvious that a rider (a student) should first have successfully completed her own mind-body learning process before beginning to lead a young horse (also a student) through a similar experience. At the Spanish Riding School, Bereiter (master rider) candidates aren't allowed to start the training of a young stallion (alongside their instructor) until after they have successfully completed their own schooling in the development of their seat and are able to competently ride their instructor's school horse.

What is commonly seen in dressage today is quite different. Riders frequently get a young horse while in the first phase of their own learning process, and then work with their riding instructor on training their horse without having developed the necessary capabilities or even attempting to. This is only partly the fault of the rider, since it is rare for good lessons in development of the seat to be offered by qualified riding instructors. We see riders getting quite far in the competitive dressage arena with serious seat errors.

I assisted a graduate of the horse farm management program of the Van Hall Institute of the Netherlands in conducting a study of the mind-body capabilities of a representative group (30) of lower-level

A well-trained school horse can give the rider the right feel for the motion of the horse.

riders. Using video of a dressage test they had all ridden, we analyzed their riding.

The study confirmed what I suspected from my experiences as a riding instructor: many riders at the lower levels still have significant weaknesses in the first phase of their own mind-body learning process. Therefore, they are not in the position to supportively ride a schoolmaster, never mind being able to bring along a green horse. In our study, riders were weakest in the aspects of balance, body control, and keeping with the horse's movement. They hindered their horses more than supported them.

Furthermore, the development of rider feel and training according to the scale principle (see p. 74) was insufficient. Since the riders generally scored "sufficient" in the areas of concentration and communication, the problems seem to lie mainly in not having experienced systematic development of their own mind-body learning process, which would have enabled them to better support the horse. The interviews confirmed that only a single participant in the study had ever had longe lessons devoted to seat development or had worked with her riding instructor specifically on improving her seat.

The predominant riding errors that hindered the horse in the planning and execution of his movements were:

1 The "chair seat" with raised calves.

2 Hands pushed low and wide.

3 Constantly "thumping" legs.

4 Overuse of the reins.

More than half of the horses were ridden overflexed with a tense back at a too fast tempo throughout the entire test. In addition, 73 percent of the tests analyzed showed an obvious lack of knowledge about biomechanical principles, which was confirmed in the interview. Interestingly, 90 percent of the riders asked were aware of their own problems with their seat and in giving the aids, but 63 percent still received a sufficient score for seat and giving the aids and the effect of the aids from the judges. Without the judges marking their deficiencies accordingly, why should they be motivated to continue to work on themselves?

1 Tipping the pelvis forward and holding the hands wide and down are common rider errors seen today.

2 The "chair seat" with calves drawn up and applying "thumping" pressure is another common rider error that significantly hinders the horse's ability to move and focus.

1

2

Optimal Conditions for Starting a Horse

Just like the rider, the horse needs to meet basic physical require-
ments before beginning the mind-body learning process. In the case
of a normal horse that has grown up in a herd, these physical require-
ments are met. Consequently, the young horse is better prepared for
the process than most beginner riders. The average beginner rider
hasn't intensively practiced another sport and is less ready to engage
in a demanding physical activity than the average horse.

*Ideally, the young horse trusts
other horses and humans before
engaging in the mind-body
learning process related to dressage training.*

The rider should frequently observe her horse in the pasture and in the herd. This allows her to learn characteristics of his personality and cultivates her ability to notice when something isn't right in the course of training him.

This is assuming the young horse has had the luck to grow up in ideal circumstances, he has lived in a group of horses of various ages and wasn't separated too early or traumatically from his mother. A mixed-age group is ideal as it provides the young horse playmates but also allows him to learn how to fit into an established social structure.

This way he develops social capabilities and knows where his place in the herd is.

In play with the other horses he learns which movements he can do easily, which are hard, and how to logically plan his movements. He therefore develops an awareness of his body and how to move. He gets to know his body well and masters the natural movement repertoire of a horse.

Unfortunately, there are many horses that don't have frequent access to interactions with other horses in a social context. Just like a child who is underdeveloped socially and physically, these horses must be well supported with remedial work before their career as a dressage horse can begin.

Even foals should trust humans enough to be near them. Introductions at this young age work best when the horse is with his mother.

The human should play a positive role for the young horse from the beginning. His mother gave him confidence. The human should be sure that his important early education allows him to continue from this point of confidence and trust people. He should allow himself to be led from the herd without panicking, and learn to accept the farrier and the veterinarian. He should allow a blanket to be put on him, shipping boots to be strapped round his legs, and be willing to travel with his mother or other horses in a horse trailer. The young horse needs to accept contact with humans and other horses. He should be curious but not pushy. He should willingly walk with a human, and let himself be touched all over when he is groomed. A relationship between human and horse begins to develop when taking walks and during grooming.

When all contact with humans from babyhood has encouraged trust, then the horse will be confident as he learns to move with and develop relationships with other horses and the people in his life. This is the ideal scenario for starting a dressage horse.

The horse shows us his natural athletic ability and temperament best when at liberty.

When the rider has watched her horse frequently in the herd and developed a feel for his personality and his athletic capabilities, then the preliminary exercises in groundwork can begin: moving him around, leading, getting him accustomed to equipment, and introducing him to longeing. This early work will all go more smoothly when the rider has observed the horse in the pasture because she is then better prepared for what is likely to occur in their "conversations."

The Rider as Athletic Trainer for the Horse

The rider should be alert for opportunities to influence her horse's mind and body and use them in the course of developing a dialogue of motion. She should be prepared to invest as much in her own mind-body development and her relationship with her horse as she is in training her horse movements. She must keep a critical eye on her own attitude. If she has been taught and supported by a good riding instructor during her own mind-body learning process, she is better prepared to support the horse as he goes through the learning phases, because she understands what the process is like. She needs to think carefully about the following concepts if she wants to be a good coach and athletic trainer for her horse:

The mind-body learning process of rider and horse

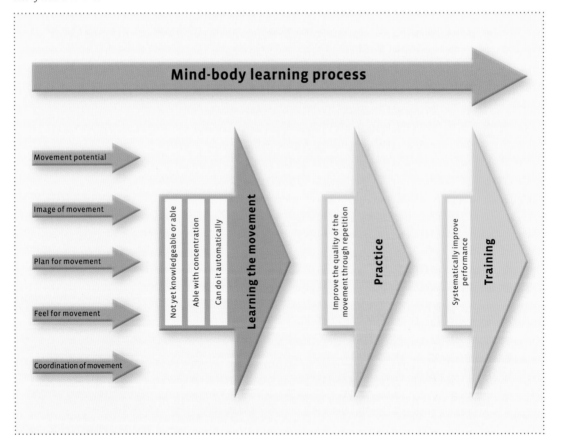

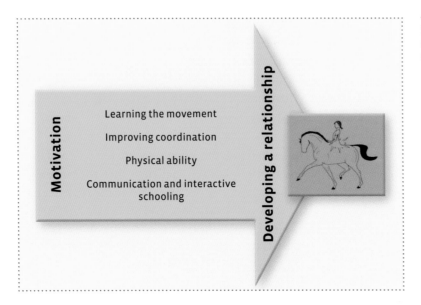

The relationship between horse and rider builds on motivation and technique.

· Mind-body connection (neurophysiology, mental aspects of learning to move).
· Training and coaching (efficient and logical increase in challenge).
· Biomechanics (anatomy, sport physiology).
· Relationship (psychology, motivation).

In the preceding chapters we have talked about the mind-body elements of "being ridden." In the chapters that follow we will address important aspects of coaching, biomechanics, and the rider-horse relationship.

Training coach

"Training" means nothing more than to develop necessary physical abilities, to further develop strengths, and to improve weaknesses. The stress placed on specific organs, such as the muscles and heart, is systematically increased in order to improve their tolerance for certain kinds of exertion. In order to understand this process and how it applies to the horse, the rider must have a basic understanding of anatomy, sport physiology, and learning psychology—for both horses and humans. In the course of training, the rider must bring coordination, timing, and feel to the equation, while the horse—like the male ballet dancer (see p. 20)—must bring endurance, speed, and power.

The work rider and horse do together must then develop these capabilities.

When a training stimulus is too strong it leads to severe fatigue (as seen in a muscle cramp), and in serious cases, it can even lead to organ damage. When the recovery phases are too brief and a workout is continued despite the horse's fatigue, then the performance level sinks.

On the other hand, when the recovery phases are too long and the training stimulus too subtle or lacking challenge, then the horse's performance level does not increase because the so-called supercompensation effect isn't achieved. The fitness level of the body in training can be segmented into four phases:

1 Initial fitness (base level).
2 Training (fitness decreases).
3 Recovery (fitness returns to initial base fitness level).
4 Supercompensation (fitness surpasses initial fitness level in anticipation of more training).

The supercompensation effect states that the body increases its performance capacity beyond its initial level during a recovery phase, and then maintains that higher level of performance for a period of time.

Note: A well measured training stimulus should not be confused with stress. Because a horse can't learn when afraid, it is illogical to train a horse under stress.

In general, young horses need 48 hours to repair the small tears in the muscle fibers that occur during training, and which can result in muscle cramps. This means that an intensive dressage ride should be compensated for the next day with a relaxing walk on the trail or a light jog on the longe line. It is reasonable to take a long quiet ride at the walk, trot, or slow canter, or to move quietly long and low in correct lines in the arena.

The rider shouldn't work on building the strength or coordination needed for collection and then go trotting or galloping around at a high rate of speed. Endurance training, for example, should be separated from work on coordination and power. Change is good for maintaining motivation in the horse, but should be reasonable in what it requests and systematically built into the training program.

1 *It is a sign of muscle fatigue when the young horse lifts his head high during a riding session. Don't ride against his inclination; instead, give his muscles a little time to recover.*

2 *Dismounting and giving the horse a break in hand is recommended.*

1

2

Strength training should be done in sets, alternating with stretching and moments of relaxation. Timed breaks are necessary for recovery and are very important for optimizing the training phases.

Collection in the horse requires power in the hindquarters that must be developed slowly, over time. Consider for example, what it would be like to climb up and down five stories of stairs in extreme deep knee bends without preparation. If, while climbing, you take a short break after every floor, your thighs will get stronger. If you climb all the floors in one go without regard for fatigue, either you won't make it, or instead of a positive training effect, you'll have muscle cramps.

Collection at a canter is especially difficult for my Friesian Hanns, with his long back and steep hindquarters. Consequently, I collect him only so long as he can and then, before he gets tired, I either take

When planning a workout that focuses on developing the coordination and strength needed in collection (here shown in hand), it isn't logical to make the horse tired in advance. A gentle loosening of his musculature and easy warm-up is sufficient.

1–3 *Training a horse in order to change his way of moving from on the forehand (1) through engagement (2) to collection (3) is very difficult and must be done systematically.*

a walk break or let him go long and low. I reward every effort on his part with a lot of enthusiasm. In this way, what is for him a difficult and unpleasant exercise becomes one he does willingly.

The dressage horse must have a great deal of power for the collection required at the Grand Prix level. Pirouettes, piaffe, and the transitions into and out of the piaffe are especially demanding. In order to meet these demands, the horse must be nurtured step by step along a careful path of conditioning, just like a runner training to run a marathon. And if the horse's conditioning must be rebuilt after a long break in training, it needs to be handled just as we would handle it for ourselves. I have experienced this myself, after first competing in a 3.7 mile (6 kilometer) run when in good condition and then again after a break due to illness.

Biomechanics: ballet en pointe for the horse

The young dressage horse is comparable to a young ballet student. The latter learns to move consciously in balance. She learns body awareness in front of the mirror. She moves according to firm rules and movement mechanics across the room. The ballet student must actively control her movements, especially in exercises at the barre,

The quality of the rider's seat is especially important when working a young horse.

by using her core for stability and balance.

When the ballet student is finally able to balance without using her hands for stability, she can begin dancing en pointe. Now, her base of support is very small. If stability through the pelvis and the lower back (the core) hasn't yet been achieved, it will be very difficult to manage the leverage that is increased during a shifting of weight.

The same goes for the young horse. He learns to consciously move on curves and in transitions, in all three gaits, and in lateral movements. The more he works in engagement toward collection, the better his ability to plan his movements must be and the more stable his balance must be, which comes from training the hindquarters, the back, and the upper neck. Like the ballet dancer beginning to move en pointe, the horse's base of support gets smaller the more collected he is.

Note: We shouldn't assume that the rider's seat is only important when the horse's "support surface" gets smaller in collection. A crooked rider on a young horse can cause the horse to move stiffly and incorrectly on curved lines. And, since all unpleasant experiences have an especially significant impact on a young horse in training, imbalances that make him feel insecure should be avoided at all costs.

The ability to take the nature of the horse into consideration while striving to understand his biomechanics is necessary to capably judge which movement patterns are functional and which are not—and this applies to the early education of the young horse on up to the training of the experienced sport horse. The biomechanics of the horse provide direction as we progress. With such knowledge at our disposal, we can logically sort through what is pleasant or unpleasant, helpful or damaging to the horse.

When the horse is grazing in the pasture, the dorsal longitudinal ligament (*Ligamentum longitudinale dorsale*), which passes along the floor of the vertebral canal from the axis (at the poll) to the sacrum (in the hind end), causes the spinous processes of the withers (the first five to nine thoracic vertebrae) to "fan out," resulting in a light stretch of the back muscles. This is a practical trait for a grazing animal, but it is also very important if the horse is to carry the weight of a rider without hindering his ability to use his back muscles.

1

2

The horse's back must be able to arch up under the rider and "swing" to allow the haunches to flex, developing an action similar to that of a coiled spring.

A similar "fanning" of the withers and stretch of the back muscles occurs when riding a young horse forward and down, and later through development of the upper neck musculature with the neck being appropriately long in all stages of engagement and collection. Only with this preparation can the horse's back musculature work undisturbed by the rider.

1

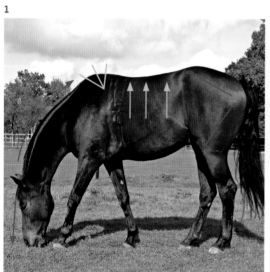

2

1–2 *Here we can see the "fanning" of the vertebrae of the withers in a grazing horse and in a horse stretched forward and downward under saddle. When ridden forward and downward, the horse's neck should be long with his nose in front of the vertical—he should not be overflexed.*

Nurturing the human-horse relationship

As we have seen, the mind-body learning process can only work when embedded in a positive relationship between rider and horse. Only when the learning itself is experienced as positive and logical can the horse be motivated to do something that he would never do on his own.

The horse appreciates it when his rider tries to understand him, is proud of him, and is happy when they have worked well together. He may not understand what we say, but how we say it is very well understood due to his social sense. So rewarding him when appropriate is logical—albeit not in a behavioristic sense (see discussion on this subject earlier—p. 37).

We shouldn't limit our interactions with our horse to workouts and training sessions.

As mentioned, we learn a lot about the horse's personality by watching him out with his herd: when and how he enjoys moving; his problem-solving patterns; how he deals with conflict; and how he acts in relationships.

It also doesn't hurt to deepen the relationship with our horses as they do with one another—through scratching and body contact. When I visit my horses in the pasture, they show me whether they are happy to be near me and have me touch them. And I can draw

Pride in our horse's performance, and the associated happiness we feel, should be shared with him. Know that the "pat" or "stroke" itself is not the reward—it is the "meaning" behind it that rewards the horse.

The rider should spend casual time with her horse outside of work sessions. This allows her to know him better and deepens their relationship.

conclusions from how willing they are to be brought in for work about how they are feeling in general, as well as the state of our relationship.

Just as with other humans, our relationship with our horse can change and must be nurtured. Poor training at any point can ruin the relationship. Consequently, it makes sense to invest in our capabilities as riders and trainers. Luckily, horses can learn to trust us again quickly. I am always fascinated when I see a poorly ridden horse that has been damaged by his rider psychologically and physically open up to her again when she changes her attitude, becomes less "predator-like," and rides in a horse-friendly way.

Many riders take "negative" signals from the horse as a personal

affront, or see an effort by the horse to preserve his balance as a deliberate and mean attempt to hurt the rider or to "test her." We often
hear a rider talk about how "unthankful" her horse is or how "he won't
work for me."

Since mankind instinctually "wants" to control, it is hard for us to
accept that since a horse is a flight animal, we can never control or
understand him 100 percent. But by developing an understanding of
the horse's flight mechanisms and processes, it is possible to work
with him. Horses have a highly developed social sense, which makes
them able to sense our true intent precisely. They instinctively sense
what a person really means and wants, even when the person doesn't
yet know in that moment! Horses feel hidden aggression and react
clearly to it. They sense insecurity or a desire to dominate just as well
as they tune in to our relaxation, security, and affection, and they
mirror these emotions in their own behavior.

Horses want clarity and harmony in their social world

Horses really want only one thing: to satisfy their natural needs as
harmoniously as possible in their social environment. They are happy
to oblige the directions of the leader or higher-ranking pasture mates,
since these interactions are very clear, nonjudgmental, and functional. They will be just as happy to oblige the humans in their life when
the humans are able to be clear, nonjudgmental, and functional in
their requests.

In my experience as a riding instructor, I frequently find riders
ascribing human motives to their horses and misinterpreting their
horse's signals. No horse pulls on the reins in order to make life hard
for his owner; he doesn't move his feet when he gets excited instead of
standing still as asked just to "show his rider." Most often, the horse
doesn't do what the rider expects because she gives him contradictory
or unclear aids, and he doesn't understand what she wants. Or, perhaps he isn't yet able to do what is being asked of him. Since the horse
craves social harmony such misunderstandings cause insecurity and
psychological stress in him.

So-called "resistances" in the horse have nothing to do with his wish "to show his rider a thing or two." When a horse protests strongly to a request from his rider, then there is surely a reason for it, which needs to be figured out.

Riding Theory: Skiing Curriculum for the Horse

What Skiing and Being Ridden Have in Common

Likening "being ridden" to learning to ski occurred to me when I started teaching my students comparative movement and the systematic evolution of training from the horse's perspective. Just as the advanced skier becomes accustomed to the sensation of gliding down a mountain on a pair of skis attached to her legs, so the dressage horse can learn to move forward with power, swing, and harmony with a rider on his back.

The skier who can use her knees and hips well and has sufficient conditioning can make skilled and fluid changes of direction, even on difficult terrain. It is the same for a dressage horse: the better the horse can shift his weight to his hindquarters by flexing his haunches and the better condition he is in, the smaller the turns (all the way up to pirouettes) he can make while maintaining impulsion and balance.

The skier usually runs into problems when she hasn't learned the proper techniques well enough, meaning she hasn't systematically practiced her skills under the tutelage of a ski instructor on the beginner slope. Or maybe she hasn't yet learned to adapt to increasingly difficult terrain and varying snow conditions. Additionally, when her physical condition isn't sufficiently developed or she is too tired to react quickly and accurately to the demands of the trail and the environment, she can find herself in trouble.

Again, it is similar for the dressage horse. Above all, both the skier and the dressage horse need a logical instruction plan that presents each new lesson as a progressive step and checks for competency before something more challenging is introduced. My "skiing curriculum" for the horse guarantees that no step is left out and assures that each learning goal is achieved before rider and horse move on.

The training steps for the dressage horse are similar to what a skier must learn in ski school.

From Ski School to Mogul Trails

The skier learns how to move and balance from the safety of the practice slope. A good ski instructor teaches the student the four most

How the Skier and the Horse Learn to Move

Skiing is a complex mind-body activity that is as difficult for humans as being ridden is for a horse. The skier develops new body awareness and movement patterns that make it possible to balance with skis on her feet. The horse develops new body awareness and movement patterns that make it possible to move in balance with a rider on his back.

The better the skier can use her hips, the better she is able to turn rhythmically. A skier can also understand how important it is for the horse to shift his weight to his hindquarters: if the skier isn't balanced back over her lower body, she can fall over her own poles because she is top heavy. She needs to learn to shove off so that her poles help maintain the fluidity of the motion but aren't used as supports—then she can move in balance. A certain level of basic conditioning, power, and endurance is required, which she gains through regular training.

The skier has certain physical capabilities to start with and must further develop these in order to be able to move from Point A to Point B in a totally different manner than usual—now with two slippery skis on her feet. She must learn to overcome other very human characteristics and instincts that can hinder her abilities on the mountain: fear of speed, fear of loss of control, and fear of heights, for example.

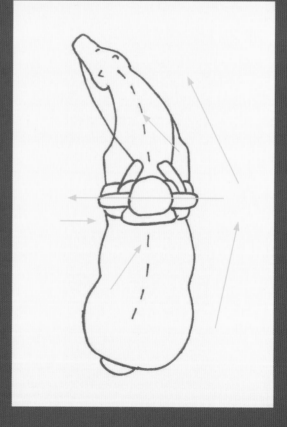

important elements of skiing using systematic and progressive exercises:

1   Controlling speed (speeding up and slowing down).
2   Turning (changing direction).
3   Steering (following a planned path from one point to another).
4   Maintaining balance (in all movements and conditions).

The same is true for the horse: he must develop and store in his "movement memory" a new and second body perception. Whether or not the horse feels good about being ridden depends on how secure he feels in the exercises he's being asked to perform. Does he learn them in the company of other horses with a responsible trainer, or does he feel like he has been recklessly thrown onto a steep icy trail covered with moguls?

Just like the skier, the horse must learn to technically adjust his ability to turn, steer, and stay in balance under changing circumstances.

Naturally, the ski instructor doesn't take his students on a steep and icy run on the first day of their ski vacation. A smart skier ensures

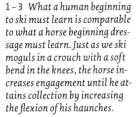

1–3 *What a human beginning to ski must learn is comparable to what a horse beginning dressage must learn. Just as we ski moguls in a crouch with a soft bend in the knees, the horse increases engagement until he attains collection by increasing the flexion of his haunches.*

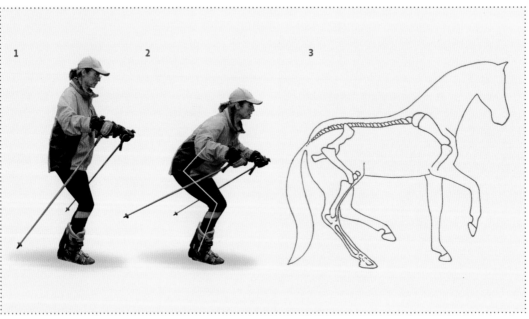

that her body is well prepared through proper gymnastic training before she gets on the slick snow with skis. In terms of the dressage horse, work in hand to mobilize the joints and longeing are the preparation he needs to prepare for more demanding workouts.

Similar to ski instruction, classical dressage training builds systematically in the following areas:

- **Learning to move:** Learning new or changed ways of moving. (In skiing, doing ski gymnastics and practicing on the bunny slope.)
- Improving coordination: Practicing in order to internalize new movement patterns. (In skiing, gliding exercises and practicing movement sequences on flat terrain.)
- **Developing physical ability:** Working on mobility, power, endurance, speed. (In skiing, endurance and strength training in the fitness center and timing training sets—for example, don't do moguls when tired or train slalom and downhill on the same day.)
- **Ensuring motivation:** Imparting and maintaining joy in new ways of moving with the rider. (In skiing, this can include different terrains and competitions, trying cross-country, participating on a ski team.)
- **Enhancing communication and interactive schooling:** Developing collaboration and a dialogue of motion with the rider. (In skiing, the ski instructor supports each individual student and treats each one with respect.)
- **Developing a relationship:** Build the horse's level of trust in his rider. (In skiing, the ski instructor builds a relationship with the students so that they trust that he won't ask anything impossible of them.)
- **Figuring out new movement concepts:** Working in collaboration with the rider at all times, even when the task at hand is difficult or challenging. (In skiing, the ski instructor must find the right way to talk with the students so that they understand him and know what he means as he explains what is expected and then helps them do it.)

Skiing moguls (a series of bumps on a trail) is an advanced level of the sport. To master moguls at a controlled tempo requires a high degree of advanced planning, coordination, and rhythm. The skier must quietly hold his upper body posture steady while flexing the hips and bending the knees deeply, allowing the legs to absorb the shock of the uneven trail.

Using the hips to absorb shock vs. achieve collection

The skier must learn to use the right muscles in a coordinated way so that her hips, knees, and ankles cushion her from the shock of uneven

1

Flexing of the "Haunches" in Skier and Horse

Like the ski instructor with a new skier, the trainer must help the horse further develop the mental and physical gifts given to him by nature. In both skiing and the training of a dressage horse, the systematic adjustment of the center of gravity plays an important role.

1 *When the skier has developed the ability to absorb shock through the movement of her hips, then she doesn't need to use her ski poles for support, which protects her shoulders from injury. Her back must be able to cushion the impact and her thigh muscles must be strong in order to work dynamically and stay balanced in a shock-absorbing position.*

2–3 *Here, we can see what happens when the skier gets too far forward.*

1–3 *This horse doesn't control his hips sufficiently, which is likely due to how he has been trained. If he were a skier, we would say he supports himself too much with his ski poles: note how he has to move around the pirouette practically using his front legs as "poles" for support. We can clearly see a lack of flexion in his haunches.*

1

Comparing what skier and horse have to learn		
Lesson	**Skier**	**Horse**
Develop a new body awareness.	Perception of body with skis.	Perception of body with a rider on his back.
Learn efficient movement techniques in balance.	Steer and change direction through bend, flexion, weight distribution, and gliding.	Turn from the hind end and not on the forehand.
Adjust weight distribution in new movements.	Change tempo while staying balanced, using spring action in the hips with an arched back and bent knees.	Ride forward and reduce the tempo actively; use the hindquarters to develop pushing and carrying power and maintain cadence.
Maintain a new balance.	Keep upper body over the center of gravity, lean away from the slope.	No longer crooked with the neck (most likely) to the outside—instead, he is so strong and coordinated that the neck scarcely needs to be used for balance.
Compensate for unusual stress on the body.	Cushion the body against terrain unevenness: arch the back and flex the knees.	Can cope with the rider's weight because the back is supple and swinging, arching and flexing in a wave-like action.
Learn to adjust hip and knee angles according to speed and the exercise.	From the basic position (light bend of the knees), shift to a crouch that is adjusted to the terrain, speed of travel, and how the hips are being used.	Can shift weight to the hindquarters, develop collection, and flex the haunches with engagement, eventually
Develop endurance, strength, and coordination.	Move from the basic shove-off to the parallel shove-off.	Progress to lateral movements and later pirouette, passage, and piaffe.
	Progress from changing directions with large arcs and a lot of slipping to controlled tight turns on any terrain.	Move in the arena in a controlled, powerful motion, maintaining balance. Collection enables controlled turns in the smallest possible space (pirouettes) and allows a powerful lengthening of the trot and canter strides.
Specialize in a discipline.	Slalom, downhill, giant slalom.	Jumping, airs above the ground.

terrain. She must actively steer in order to change speed or direction, to shove off, slide sideways, or to glide straight forward. She must firmly arch her back in order to cushion the movements of her legs

1
2

1–2 *The sideways turn of the hips by the skier is similar to lateral bend for the horse. Just as the skier should position herself in a biomechanically correct sideways posture, the horse should have bend through his whole body, and not just in the neck. Too severe a flexion in either case interrupts the flow of movement and disturbs the balance.*

elastically and keep her balance by holding her shoulders still. If she can't absorb the shock of uneven terrain in the joints of the legs, then all the jolts will directly impact her vertebral discs.

It is the same for the horse. Having a rider on his back massively changes his balance and ability to bend and flex. As discussed, in contrast to the human, the horse doesn't move vertically but horizontally, and in dressage he must carry the weight of the rider on his back. Nevertheless the back muscles are supposed to "swing" and be supple, with the right amount of tautness, just like the skier. Just as the skier arches her back, so must the horse round his back in a horizontal arc that absorbs shock and swings with the amplitude of the movement, connecting the motion of the hind and forelegs. The horse must shift the weight on his forehand back toward the hind legs in order to turn more or less on his hindquarters. Picture the skier who pushes mostly with her legs, even if she now and then must use her poles as "front legs" to support her rhythm and balance.

"Ski Gymnastics" for the Dressage Horse: Work on the Longe Line

Just as it isn't smart to go straight from the desk to the ski trail without having prepared ourselves mentally and physically, it also isn't logical to just jump on our horse and ask him to get right to work. Mobilizing the joints through work in hand and longeing are ideal mind-body preparatory exercises used in classical training.

The horse can be slowly prepared—without experiencing pain and tension—to carry the rider through work on the longe line. Just as the skier learns that his ski instructor will help him on the bunny slope with the right exercises and instruction, a well longed horse learns that his trainer will help him to be better able to move around a circle. In addition, stepping over exercises in hand show the horse how he can best initiate changes in direction by stepping diagonally with the inside hind leg under the body.

On the longe line the horse can learn how to move in different ways and strengthen his movement apparatus so he is prepared to keep his balance under a rider. Here we can see he is stretching/reaching forward, "fanning" his withers, and stepping well under his body with his inside hind leg.

The horse learns to stretch into the outside rein, to arch his back and "swing" the long back muscle from the hindquarters while stretching forward and downward. Flexing, bending, and back activity in all three gaits can be developed on the longe line (the bunny slope for the horse) without the weight of the rider. He can also learn how to lengthen and shorten his steps. Once this repertoire of movement patterns, mobility, power, and conditioning is established, he can move from the bunny slope to the intermediate ski trail with the rider on his back.

Before the horse is constrained by side reins on the longe line, he should be allowed to stretch and warm up.

Well managed longeing can accomplish so much, including:

- Psychological gain, such as trust and willingness to communicate with the human.
- Experience that humans are helpful.
- Physical development of the body.
- Improved coordination.
- An understanding of the role of the rider in the horse-and-rider collaboration.
- The desire to stretch to the bit.
- A movement plan that depends on the trainer rather than visual orientation.
- Ability to turn on the hind legs.
- Bend throughout the body.
- Engagement of the hindquarters.
- Suppleness and relaxation.
- "Swinging" of the back.
- More activity coming out of a quiet jog.
- Familiarity with the stretch position forward and downward.
- Activation of the hindquarters.
- Back activity without a load on the back.
- A new sense of balance.
- Conditioning and muscle development.
- Improved mobility of the joints.
- Strengthening of the ligaments and tendons.
- Acclimation to a training structure: preparation, warm-up, training phase, cool-down, and care after a workout.
- Development of confidence in the training process and the trainer.

Changing how the horse moves around curves

On the longe line, the horse is confronted for the first time with the need to change how he goes around a curve. Instead of maintaining his balance by stretching his neck to the outside, he must bring his inside hind leg under his center of gravity in order for the inside shoulder to use the hind leg as a pivot point. And he must be straight, even on the circle. Longeing addresses three important elements of training: straightening, moving around curves, and transferring weight off the forehand to the hindquarters.

When the dressage horse continues to move around curves as he would naturally, he maintains his natural crookedness, and this is damaging to his health in the long run. Work on the longe line, in a large circle (18 to 20 meters), is ideal for teaching the horse the three important elements named above.

This young horse is properly outfitted for starting work on the longe line.

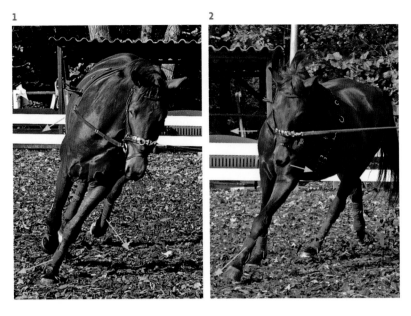

1

2

1–2 When a horse travels crookedly on a circle at a high rate of speed, centrifugal force acts on his body and is at the least uncomfortable and at the most injurious. Note how this horse's body is going in all different directions (see arrows). The horse must learn to bend through his body, stepping well under his center of gravity with his inside hind leg instead of just pulling his head to the inside.

When the horse is allowed to run loose in an arena or round pen, his natural crookedness is not corrected. He orients visually to the wall or the fence and usually tries to run along it. Since the horse is narrower at the shoulders than at the hips, he will travel crookedly along the wall. To maintain soundness as a dressage horse, he must be straightened.

Longeing builds the horse's trust in his trainer, and it develops the dialogue of motion in a scenario that is comfortable and secure for both parties. When the rider gets on the horse after several weeks of longeing, the horse will be better balanced, will understand that the rider can help him find a new balance, and will comprehend the primary aids much better. The horse will also have learned to think about his movements and plan them.

"Ski equipment" for the young dressage horse

It doesn't make sense to teach a horse to longe in a round pen since it encourages the horse's tendency to orient himself visually along the fence line—as we've discussed. It is reasonable, however, to create a separate 20- by 20-meter square within a larger arena in order to contain the horse should something go wrong.

When longeing, the length of the side reins must be gradually adjusted to suit the horse's level of training and pace while taking steps toward attaining the desired frame.

As the horse is better educated and conditioned, his hind legs come further under his, he elevates his forehand more, and the side reins can then be shortened slightly.

When first beginning a longeing program, the longeing cavesson should be used—fastened correctly and not too tightly. Since the horse can't yet move in balance, longeing in a snaffle bit could irritate his mouth. The cavesson allows us to introduce halts through pulses on the line that the horse feels on his nasal bone. The surcingle and the side reins can be added when the horse:

- Has learned to move quietly on the circle.
- Understands the purpose of the longe whip aid to activate the hind legs and doesn't run away from it.
- Accepts connection with the trainer's hand and activates his hind legs, resulting in impulsion.

The side reins are the only auxiliary equipment that can be—when used correctly—helpful in teaching the horse to stretch to the bit and control his outside shoulder. Any reins or "training aids" that pull down on the mouth or the poll hinder the horse's confidence and willingness to stretch to the bit since they cause the horse pain, interrupt the extent and range of his movement, and assure that the horse does exactly the opposite of what we want: roll the neck more or less up and behind the vertical. He will also use the muscles underneath and on the side of his neck to avoid pressure or pain on his mouth, prohibiting suppleness and relaxation. Therefore, the Gogue, "triangle reins" (Vienna sliding side reins), Pessoa Chambon, and other inventions are not recommended, even if they are advertised as elastic, a means of lengthening the neck, or "horse-friendly."

When beginning longe training in side reins, they should be fastened long enough so that the horse can stretch forward and downward into the contact, while still being able to react when he needs to rebalance himself with neck (which at this point, will still be his "balancing rod"). Compared to conventional reins in the hands of a rider, side reins have a big disadvantage in that they don't allow the horse's natural "nodding" head movement at the walk. Therefore, they shouldn't be used at the walk early in training and must not be fastened too tightly at the walk later on. It is important to adjust the length of the side reins according to the pace, as well as the horse's level of education and conditioning.

The longe line should feel similar to a regular rein in the trainer's hands and should be able to glide easily through the hands—no knots or "donuts."

I recommend using a vaulting whip as a longe whip as I find it allows the trainer to stand quietly in the middle of the longe circle while communicating to the horse via the smallest of impulses from the whip.

Here we can see the horse traveling straight on a curve with a slight bend through his body. The relaxed tail that swishes with the rhythm of the trot shows us how his supple back "swings."

Auxiliary aids that use downward pressure on the horse's mouth or poll disturb the development of good contact and should not be used.

Turning on the "Bunny Slope": Longeing over Cavalletti

Cavalletti work can help improve the horse's back activity; increase the mobility of the horse's joints and their ability to serve as "shock absorbers"; and make it easier for the horse to learn to stretch from the hind legs over the back to the bit.

That said, these positive effects are only achieved when the horse is straight, the tempo isn't too fast, and the interval between the

cavalletti is adjusted appropriately to suit both the tempo and goal of the work.

The first thing a young dressage horse must learn to do is let his neck relax down, opening and "fanning" the vertebrae of the withers as he stretches forward and downward. When the horse can work with more engagement, stabilizing his movement more through the muscles of his neck than the ligaments of the vertebral column, his back will arch up. Over cavalletti, the horse's control over his own movements will continually improve. I always have rows of trot and canter cavalletti in my arena and use them regularly in warm-up, both on the longe line and with a rider. I also use them when I need to gain the horse's concentration or relax and supple his back more quickly.

Note: I do not advise working with loose ground poles since they can cause unnecessary injury if the horse steps on them or hits them.

When working over cavalletti, select the tempo that encourages the horse to stretch forward and downward, optimally improving back activity.

Note how the tempo is too fast here: the horse has dropped his back and is using his neck to balance.

Even when just walking over cavalletti, the horse begins to concentrate on them and senses how he needs to adjust the length and height of his step. This is just like the beginner skier who learns how to coordinate knee and hip movements on the gradual decline of the bunny slope. It is important that:

1 The side reins are not adjusted too short since the horse must be able to balance with his neck if he needs to.

2 The tempo is not too fast.

Only when the horse is traveling comfortable can he think about the movement sequence necessary when going over cavalletti and learn how to move his four legs (and the rest of his body) in a quiet, round way, rhythmically over the poles.

To begin, I place no more than six cavalletti in a straight line outside the longe circle, first laid at intervals suited to the horse's walk. I then send the horse over them several times. The horse quickly learns to find the right stride length as he enters the cavalletti and makes necessary adjustments along the way—in other words, he discovers how to plan his movement independently.

When the horse keeps his focus over the walk cavalletti, stays calm, and moves with controlled and fluid steps and a lowered neck, then I move him back to the circle and work on walking correctly on the curve (see note about side reins at the walk on p. 115). Now and then I increase the activity of his inside hind leg, asking him to bend and take contact on the longe line. Then I warm him up in a quiet trot.

Before I ask the horse to go over trot cavalletti, I make sure that the tempo of the gait is right—not too fast or too slow—and then give him the chance to stretch out of a good turn forward and downward, asking him to turn using his hind end rather than over his forehand, before sending him down the line of cavalletti. After the cavalletti, I look for another correct turn with his weight over the hindquarters as he comes back on the longe circle. In principle, my support for the quality of the turn before the cavalletti row is critical to the horse being able to go correctly over the cavalletti and whether or not their desired training effect is achieved. When the horse comes out of the turn crooked and at a too fast tempo, or if I have done something wrong coordinating my activating whip aid with contact to the horse's mouth, then the horse is forced to balance himself incorrectly and simply "save himself" over the poles. Therefore, work over the cavalletti also teaches the trainer good coordination and proper timing and application of the aids.

A longeing session should only last, at the most, 20 to 30 minutes. Only about a third of the lesson should be spent on cavalletti work, since the intense concentration and coordination of movement necessary for traversing cavalletti is very demanding to the horse.

Later in training I will increase the demands on the horse's balance. For example, I might let the horse transition to the canter after the trot cavalletti row, canter a circle, then transition to trot in the correct tempo and go over the cavalletti again. In this way, rider and horse learn to "figure things out" together with increasingly difficult challenges.

Small gymnastic jumps can also be included in cavalletti workouts. Note: when incorporating gymnastics, side reins should not be used.

Twenty minutes of longe work is sufficient, since a good lesson requires intense concentration on the horse's part.

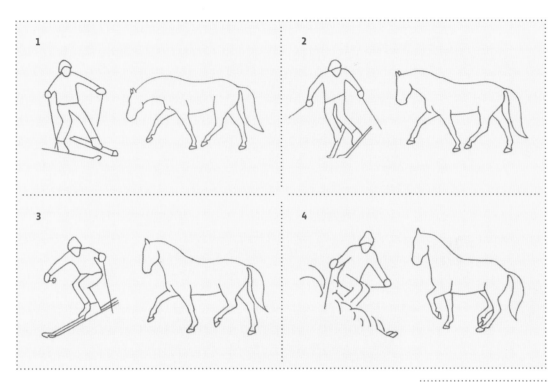

1–4 *These drawings depict the progressive training phases of a skier and a dressage horse, using a systematic and biomechanically correct instruction plan.*

Gymnastic jump routines that encourage the horse to think and improve his balance include: trot over cavalletti, jump from the trot, and trot again over cavalletti; or jump from a hand gallop, transition to trot, and go over the cavalletti.

My horses really like cavalletti work. I praise them for every independent correction and every acceptance of my aids. The better the horse understands the training goal for the exercise, the less I have to do to correct tempo and stride length. Still, as the trainer I am responsible for guiding the horse in a way that enables him to master the cavalletti independently while staying balanced and relaxed in a correct turn.

Even as a ski instructor, I frequently (and happily) worked on my own technique back on the practice slope. And so I take my horses that are already well trained back to their "practice slope" with these exercises. This is a nice change of pace for the horse and continues to develop his feel for motion, even if he is a more developed dressage horse.

From the "Bunny Slope" to the "Intermediate Trail"

The horse's back, neck, and croup musculature develops correctly when he is comfortable with the new movement patterns he has learned on the longe; when he has learned to transfer his weight to and find his balance over his hindquarters; when he moves with a pure rhythm and a relaxed back that flexes and swings in supple "waves"; and when he puts each leg down on the ground straight without twists or sideways tangents.

Remember that early in training, the horse will need to use his neck for balance again and again. Consequently, the side reins must allow him to do so momentarily and then invite him to seek contact with the bit again. Also, it is not necessarily bad when he lifts his head

Correct control of the horse's movement doesn't come from pulling the head down and forcing the horse to yield. The horse must stabilize his own head position with his developing upper neck musculature as his hind end gets stronger.

up occasionally, as long as he then readjusts and rebalances, shifting his weight evenly back over his hindquarters.

The old-school military riders knew that they should get off a young horse as soon as he threw his head up. It was a sign that the horse's back hurt. They simply allowed some rest time for the back to recover, and then rode on. In the modern way of riding, people instead try to make the horse round and deep in front, preventing him from throwing up his head and accepting that the horse suffers pain behind in the process. In this round and deep posture the bascule of the back cannot truly develop, the horse cannot improve his engagement, and the haunches cannot optimally flex.

> Bascule is a French term for "scales" or "balance." When riding horses, it can refer to the arch of the horse's back, or the arc of his body over a jump.

Mounting for the First Time

Before a green horse is mounted for the first time, his back and croup musculature should be so far developed that he can flex his haunches to some degree and carry the rider's weight without "negative" tension. The horse's head should not be tied down in front, nor should he be ridden on too short a rein. When starting the first ride on the longe line, side reins adjusted quite long may provide a sense of security to some horses, while others handle the first ride better on the longe without side reins.

When you have started the horse with work on the longe as I have described on the pages prior, the first ride is often easier if the horse is on the longe line with his trainer, as usual; once mounted (by his trainer or an assistant), the longe line offers support so the horse can slowly grow accustomed to a rider's aids. Through the experience of learning to move on the longe line without a rider first, the horse will have confidence, knowing he will be able to balance with the help of his human—even with the addition of a rider on his back.

It is helpful when mounting for the first time for the horse to stand quietly on the longe line in a relaxed environment with people he trusts around—this ensures he feels comfortable and doesn't get excited. At the Spanish Riding School in Vienna the horse is given some oats when first mounted. In this way, the horse connects being

The horse that has been well prepared on the longe line also already knows how to step further under his body with his hind legs, and again, he can do so with the rider in the saddle.

A young horse that has already learned to move "over the back" and to bend correctly on the longe line can quickly learn to do so under the rider.

mounted with the pleasure of eating. The presence of the oats also helps us gauge the horse and whether he is nervous or not. When the horse isn't relaxed enough we can wait until he exhibits signs of confidence and contentment before getting on.

As we have discussed, the horse can only have a positive learning experience when relaxed. If a horse is stressed, he can't think clearly enough to learn how to consciously plan his movement and then "store" the positive experience in his central nervous system "memory bank." Especially with young horses, we should never risk continuing to work when the horse is under stress or feeling insecure. It is therefore especially important at this stage of training to carefully control the schooling area environment.

The rider of young or green horses must be extremely well prepared in terms of her seat and stay 100 percent with the horse while in the saddle. A lack of concentration in the rider, as mentioned, is bad when working with a well-trained horse, but it unsettles the young horse significantly more. The rider must make sure that the young horse doesn't feel "abandoned." My own horse Tommy demonstrated the importance of this rule during this phase of training: When his rider stopped "riding," he bucked and tossed her over his shoulder in an elegant "judo move." She climbed back on and worked on concentrating more on the horse and her job to support him in the dialogue of motion, and Tommy never did that again.

Primary aids make moving from the "bunny slope" to the "intermediate trail" easier

Since classical riding uses the primary aids (see p. 59), the young horse quickly and instinctively discovers how the dialogue of motion works. He experiences the rider and her suggestions, which come via the movement impulses she gives, as support for accomplishing his job.

None of the horses that I have taught to ride in this way have found it necessary to buck, balk, or shy. All have entered into this new motion interaction with great trust. When the horse feels he must defend

Occasional episodes of boisterous or fearful behavior under saddle are quite normal with young horses, so always wear a riding helmet! However, it should be noted that when a horse consistently protests by bucking or shying, then we must find out what has gone wrong in his training and go back and fix it.

When we try to get the horse to yield by applying pressure on his mouth, we get the opposite: the horse braces. Auxiliary aids such as draw reins that hold the horse's head down result in the same response.

himself or shies out of fear, then something has gone wrong in the training process, and we should start over with teaching the horse movement and how to manage it on the longe line.

The green horse can learn to change pace and tempo while relaxed and in balance on the longe line. He can learn how to use his neck to regain his balance in emergencies—and the rider should allow for this. The neck serves as the horse's "balancing rod" in this phase of training more than later on. It is used in the horse's movement plan to make up for hind-end weakness and misjudgments on curves and in changes of speed, pace, and tempo.

When the rider doesn't force the horse into an uncomfortable neck position in order to get him to "yield," the horse will easily and quickly learn to plan his movement. Since horses have significant "movement intelligence" (the ability to integrate perception with action), they can assess better than the human what they need to do with their body in order to move comfortably and in a balanced manner.

Since we as riders benefit from the horse's movement intelligence, so why would we want to inhibit it? It is important that we aren't too frequently the cause of him "depending on his ski poles" for balance.

Should Classical Riding Teachings Be Changed?

The "little tyke position" was promoted in an attempt to re-form the time-tested system used in ski instruction.

We have seen how training a dressage horse step by step and according to classical guidelines is logical since they take into account the psychological and physical nature of the horse. In the last few hundred years, horses really haven't changed in their nature except for a few adaptations by breeders. So why are classical riding teachings being questioned today? Is our motivation really to make training "better" or is there something else behind it? And is it possible to make dressage training better, shorter, or simpler without sacrificing important stages of development on the part of the horse?

Are revolutionary changes in methodology useful?

At the time I was training to be a ski instructor, something similar to what is happening in dressage sport today happened in the ski industry. Someone decided to reform the traditional, tried-and-tested ski instruction methodology. What had been used to teach skiing, from the most general concepts down to the smallest details of technical exercises, for many years, was suddenly seen as no longer necessary. A very successful Austrian trainer at the top echelon of the sport decided to completely "rewrite the manual" on how we teach skiing.

This trainer started from the perspective that children learned skiing much more easily and naturally than adults. He analyzed meticulously how children learn to ski and translated that to a ski school for adults, with the intention of shortening and simplifying the learning process for adults. This way, many more skiers could be trained more quickly, which was an interesting idea to those in the business of ski tourism. Under economic pressure, the trainer's new plan was instituted despite the resistance of very experienced professionals.

For several years ski instructors and students were forced into the so-called "little tyke position" and had to struggle to accommodate the related and unnatural deep bending via the hips and knees, which

I see "hyperflexion" as the equivalent of the "little tyke position" for the horse.

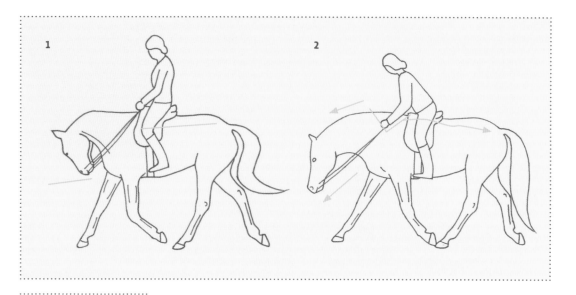

1 When the horse's neck experiences extreme shortening and flexing, the vertebrae of his withers don't "fan" (see p. 96) and the back musculature doesn't relax. This is not developmental progress for the horse.

2 When the intention is to train in a horse-friendly manner, the biomechanically practical stretch into the forward-and-downward position cannot be skipped.

works well for small children, but not really with the movement patterns of an adult.

It was difficult to train myself to ski using the new techniques, as they worked against my own body feel, but I wanted to work as a ski instructor and had to pass the test. When teaching, I continued to be uncomfortable in the forced position and the methodical structure didn't work for my students as promised. But I blamed myself when something didn't go right.

Luckily, this new method with its "little tyke position" didn't fulfill expectations and was quickly removed from the official ski instruction manual. People had recognized that the traditional, proven techniques, with all the different variations to fit the terrain and discipline, were really quite good. We found that we can't teach skiing to adults by imitating children—an adult human has psychological and physical capabilities, as well as anatomical realities, that just can't be ignored.

Developments in sports medicine and science can of course work out details and nuances that refine training, especially when we reach levels at the top of our respective sport. However, revolutionary changes to fundamentals have never been shown to be necessary or successful.

The "little tyke position" for the horse

Just as the nature of the human is the starting point for his training as a skier, so it is with the horse when training him for dressage. We can't outwit nature without causing damage. We can't work against the body as it exists and omit learning steps or necessary stages of exercise. We can't develop muscle and conditioning without injury to the two- or four-legged athlete except through systematic and slowly increased demands, with reasonable breaks for recovery. Even the very talented and physically gifted athlete cannot afford to stray from daily, progressive, reasonable, varied training, if he or she wants to stay healthy, enjoy the experience, and minimize frustration and incidences of injury.

The correct "frame" for training and for competition

The fact that breeding has given us better and better sport horses leads dressage riders to believe they can shorten or skip their own learning process by simply buying a good horse. Likewise, a horse's expressive front end leads people to forget about the necessary flexing of his hindquarters. With horses that are naturally built uphill and gifted with good movement, people try to go from the "bunny slope" straight to the "advanced ski run." Such a crazy decision on the mountain would likely end up with the skier over a cliff. In dressage, the horse is forced to compensate for a lack of conditioning with unnatural and damaging physical positions. Sooner or later this injures him—physically and mentally.

Incorrect positions and motion sequences, comparable to the "little tyke position" in skiing, have been integrated into horse training according to the idea that an extreme bending or rolling up of the horse's neck improves the overall training effect, strengthens the horse, and shortens the amount of time it takes to bring along a dressage prospect. At this point it makes sense to point out that the posture used in training should match that required at a particular stage of competition. Using hyperflexion as a training posture doesn't comport with the guidelines required for competitions. Using it is like a skier training to race the slalom using a completely different technique than what he can use in competition.

Here we see the different stages and frames as the horse develops self-carriage using the classical system of horse-friendly training.

People expect to achieve amazing results by using hyperflexion, the recent "wonder position" seen in dressage; however, this posture runs counter to what we know about equine biomechanics; it leads to incorrect motion sequences on the part of the horse; and it greatly limits the horse's ability to perform, both physically and psychologically.

The Classical Training Scale: The Means to Achieving Self-Carriage

How Riding Can Be Fun for the Horse

In many ways horses have been and still are "broken in" and work under force and fear. However, it is totally possible for the horse to joyfully participate in riding sports—in being "dance partners" with a rider.

The horse shows us this is possible clearly and distinctly via his most natural form of expression: body language. We humans experience a relaxed horse that is working happily as aesthetically pleasing, but we usually can't figure out what actually instigates the feeling of harmony when we see it, or when we feel it when riding.

As riders we do notice when we get tense and our horse has a corresponding response. If we can then manage to relax ourselves, the horse responds the same way throughout his whole body and even with contented (and audible) sighs. He is happier. Luckily, the Classical Training Scale helps us achieve this "happier" state.

How a horse moves shows how he feels

Balance, movement, and feeling are inseparable in the horse. If we humans learn to put ourselves in the horse's position and to feel what the horse feels, we can begin to notice immediately when he feels good about what we are doing or not. We should be able to "touch base" in this way regardless of whether we are riding a dressage test, longeing, out trail riding, or watching while the horse runs free and plays.

When we understand what the horse is telling us with his body language, what moods are expressed by certain body positions and in how he is moving, we know quite clearly what we have done correctly or incorrectly as his trainer.

It is important to learn to differentiate between signs of tension, strain, and relaxation, and to recognize when motion flows and when it is blocked somewhere. We could say "how a horse feels is shown in how he moves," as well as turn it the other way around: "How the horse moves shows how he feels."

We can see this from the ground and feel it directly from the saddle. It is a prerequisite for harmony that the horse be mentally and physically balanced. The Classical Training Scale refers to Suppleness, which also means a relaxed state of mind.

Horses express how they feel "inside" through physical movement.

This horse is physically and mentally balanced, as exhibited by his movement and expression.

Indicators of Well-being

The Classical Training Scale, the guidelines for teaching the dressage horse, is the "ski instruction manual" for the horse. The Scale offers evaluative criteria that allow us to assess if a horse has been trained and is being ridden true to its guidelines, and also if he is comfortable being ridden.

The difficulty of the exercises that a horse is capable of performing says nothing about whether the criteria of the Scale are met. A Grand Prix horse can fulfill several or none of the indicators, while a horse at the lowest level can fulfill all of them. In this case, the lower-level horse is the better trained of the two.

We can conclude from how the horse moves and his expression whether or not he is in a harmonious dialogue of motion with his rider. The "well-being criteria" of the scale are:

- Rhythm
- Suppleness
- Impulsion
- Straightness
- Contact
- Increased engagement to Collection
- Throughness

The listing of the criteria of the Scale does not mean that first Rhythm must be there, then Suppleness, then Impulsion, and so on. They should all be present at the same time when the horse is ridden since they are all closely connected. Naturally, a young horse can't be collected yet, but the early stages of Collection, increased engagement, should be the goal from the very first ride.

The Classical Training Scale, when combined with the ability of the rider, leads to the harmony for which we strive. When the foundation or even one column is lacking, then the whole building falls down.

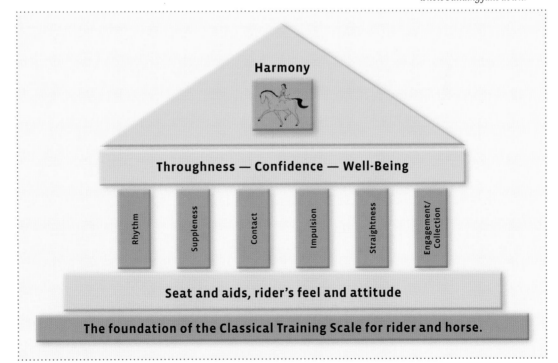

Harmony

Throughness — Confidence — Well-Being

Rhythm · Suppleness · Contact · Impulsion · Straightness · Engagement/Collection

Seat and aids, rider's feel and attitude

The foundation of the Classical Training Scale for rider and horse.

The meaning of each Training Scale criterion is given in this chart, which compares different points of view. The fundamental idea is that the dialogue of motion between rider and horse should flow in balance and without blockage. The horse should be open to the suggestions of his rider for additional movement planning, which he willingly accepts as his own. This is only possible for him when he feels comfortable.

What the Classical Training Scale Means

	Training	Movement
Rhythm	Balance	Control of the rhythm shows that the horse's body is in balance and that he can consciously move with regularity. The back can swing equally from side to side. The movement amplitude and the rhythm stay the same with changes of tempo, direction, stride length, and gait.
Suppleness	Relaxation in body and mind	The young or green horse should drop his neck from the withers in a forward-and-downward stretch in order to be able to swing relaxed over the back. Later, the back will be relieved by the development of the horse's upper neck musculature, which causes the vertebrae of the withers to "fan" during engagement and Collection while maintaining sufficient neck length. The back can arch and swing. Signs of Suppleness and relaxation are loose swinging of the hip musculature and the lower neck muscles; back amplitude (extent of movement side to side); and cadenced, round movement.
Impulsion	Active forward tendency	Through spring-like flexion in the joints of the hindquarters, the horse can shift from "pushing power" to "carrying power," and he can develop the ability to lengthen his stride out of impulsion. His movements are springy, calm, powerful, and cadenced.
Contact	Horse stretches to the bit and doesn't go behind it	Arched "positive" tension develops from the hindquarters over the horse's back to the poll and mouth, but doesn't disturb the amplitude of the swing in the horse's back.
Straightness	Straighten the narrower forehand to the wider hindquarters	Straightening the horse's body on straight or curved lines allows free flow of his movement from the hindquarters through to the poll and mouth.
Engagement	Hindquarters step increasingly under the center of gravity	The increasing engagement of the hindquarters from the hips (haunches) as the hind legs step further under the center of gravity of horse and rider.
Collection	Flexing of the haunches	Development of power in the muscles and improved mobility of the joints (hips, stifles, hocks).
Throughness	Physical and mental openness to suggestions of the rider	The horse's joints appear to "spring" through functional tightening and relaxing of his musculature while his back swings.

Mind-body Significance	Meaning for the Horse	Finding a "Frame" of Well-being
Conscious control—not reactive but planned. The horse can only travel in a good rhythm when he can balance himself undisturbed.	The horse balances himself differently under the rider and on the longe line. The horse can control his balance by planning his movement using his new way of traveling around curves. Moving in rhythm gives the horse security.	The rider helps the horse find the right tempo and balance. She adjusts herself to the natural rhythm of the horse and helps him to balance in the right tempo, with the right degree of movement amplitude and length of frame.
The horse must not brace or cramp the muscles of his back or under his neck. He shouldn't strain to correct his movements or reactively correct his balance. His motion is fluid and he concentrates on his communication and movement tasks with his rider.	The horse trusts his rider who supports him as he maintains his physical and mental balance. The horse should not defensively brace anywhere in an attempt to avoid pain.	The rider helps the horse relax. She should not get tense or interrupt the flow of motion or she will unbalance the horse or hurt him. She gives her aids as supporting impulses for types of movement. From this point of shared balance the horse can simply "swing and spring" and focus on the different movements that specific exercises require.
The horse shows powerful but round, quiet but active movements at a suitable tempo with springy, supple joints. The horse thinks ahead; he anticipates the next planned movement.	Without rushing, the horse can move with spring when his stride is shortened and increase ground cover in the extended paces. This feels pleasant and enjoyable to both horse and rider.	The horse accepts the frame that corresponds to his gait, pace, and tempo. When stretching his neck out, the frame as a whole must lengthen. At the walk, his natural head nod should not be interrupted. Impulsion develops a swinging back from the spring of his flexed haunches.
The horse accepts the bit as an aid to achieve the right arched "positive" tension and activity of the back.	He can accept the bit as a pain-free aid that conveys signals for lifting the back, and he can communicate through it with the rider. He demonstrates through a relaxed chewing whether or not the rider is correctly supporting him.	The horse stretches his upper neck musculature toward the bit and chews with satisfaction. He reacts softly with an open jaw angle when the amplitude of his body's movement goes through to the poll. The horse's nose remains in front of or on the vertical.
The horse learns to balance himself on curves with a movement of the hips and by stepping under his body diagonally instead of putting his neck to the outside or becoming crooked in the neck. Movements flow through the whole body, which swings as a unit. There is a feeling of fluidity. The mobility of the horse improves from the beginning of engagement to optimal Collection. The quality of spring, lightening of the forehand, and fluidity of motion improve. Power improves, as well, and the horse gains self-confidence and the feeling that he can do more.	The horse trusts the rider's support of his movement plan and no longer orients himself visually or falls into periods of natural crookedness.	The horse steps with the inside (inside the bend) hind leg diagonally under his center of gravity and can easily align his outside shoulder with his hindquarters while shifting his weight onto them. The joints of the forehand are not loaded excessively; as he moves straight, his springy movement flows perfectly through his whole body.
In one, fluid motion, the horse can concentrate on both the rider's movement impulses and the execution of the desired movement at the same time without stress.	The horse realizes that he has improved freedom of movement and maneuverability; he is powerfully engaged with "positive" tension in the haunches and the back.	The flexion of the horse's hindquarters is spring-like from the hips to the hocks and compresses to a degree that is appropriate for his level of training.
	He can accept more weight on his hind end; for example, turns on the haunches are possible. His ability to control his balance and movement continue to improve.	
	Complete harmony with the rider (a good relationship) and fluid motion give the horse a pleasant sense of what it can be like to work in a social context.	A wavelike movement of the horse's back is evident, and there aren't any apparent resistances or blockages from his hind legs all the way to his mouth. The horse is able to adjust the degree to which his back swings according to the wishes of the rider.

Preserving the Amplitude of the Horse's Movement

The Classical Training Scale has a solid foundation: the horse's movement plan, the amplitude of the horse's motion, and the horse's balance must not be disturbed. Only under these conditions can the basic elements of the Scale be fulfilled. Since they are all interdependent, we have a "chicken-egg" situation.

Tempo and rhythm directly affect the amplitude of the horse's movement: If both are right and the horse is supple, then "swing" can move from the hind leg to the nose without interruption, as is visible in this photograph. When the tempo is too fast or the horse is "blocked" by the rider's hands or seat, the movement can't be optimal.

Identify the rate of motion that is comfortable for the horse
Horses frequently try to compensate for insufficient technique or
insecurity with increased speed. But it is exactly that increased speed
that hinders the supple, wavelike movement over the horse's back for
which we strive and leads to tension and pain in his body. In this
scenario, the horse frequently ends up on the forehand and out of
balance. Consequently, establishing the correct tempo (rate of motion
or repetition of the rhythm) is necessary for a happy horse.

Sometimes it is necessary to let the horse jog slowly to relax him,
stretch him, and enable him to open and "fan" the withers (see p. 96).
From this relaxed state, more activity of the hindquarters can be
developed without hindering the back's motion.

On the other end of the spectrum, when the horse is relying on the
muscles under his neck, stiffening the back and moving in a too-fast
tempo, we should ride forward to maintain the tempo and not let it
get too fast. I notice with all my students that it helps them sense
changes in tempo when they concentrate on whether the movement
of the horse's legs and the back are round and elastic. Every horse has
his own basic tempo and way of "swinging" through his body. The
rider must learn to feel and see these differences.

*A relaxed trot in a stretching
frame early in training.*

Enable balance

There is an exercise I like to help make clear how important it is for the horse to be able to use his neck as a balancing rod: When we walk on a balance beam, it is extremely important for us to feel that we can use our two arms to balance at any time (see photos p. 137). When our arms are tied behind our back, it is very difficult to stay on the balance beam. We fall out of balance more often or our muscles cramp. If, however, we are told that we have to keep our hands behind our back but they aren't fastened, and we are allowed to use them in an emergency for balance, then the frequency of muscle cramping and falling out of balance is drastically reduced. This is because we know that we can use our arms to balance should we need them.

The horse is in the same situation when he is ridden in the "classical contact" (in front of the vertical and with sufficient neck length). He is able to use his "balancing rod"—his neck—whenever he needs to catch his balance, and then he can pick up the contact again as soon as he regains it. However, when a horse is held in a shortened neck position by the rider's hands, he doesn't have that ability. This is comparable to us having our hands tied behind our back. Think about it: police bind prisoners' hands behind their back with handcuffs so they can't run away—their feet are free, but their balance is compromised.

When the reins act as "handcuffs" on the horse, they not only prevent him from balancing himself, but also cause instinctive fear in a flight animal, since he feels that he can't run away if necessary.

Contact should come from the horse—he should stretch elastically into the reins rather than yielding to the rider's hands.

Comfortable contact

The comfort of the connection between horse and rider depends directly on the availability of the "balancing rod" neck we just discussed. And remember, the horse takes the contact. In several modern schools of riding, correct contact is replaced with the horse yielding at the poll and going behind the vertical in response to pressure from the rider's hands. This is a completely different relationship between the rider's hands and the horse's mouth than that of classical theory.

Since we want the horse to develop and use his upper neck musculature in order to optimally unburden his back, yielding in the poll is not possible unless the horse also opens and "fans" the vertebrae of

Balance Exercise for the Rider

1 – 3 *The horse's ability to use his "balancing rod" neck defines the horse's balance and instills confidence in his use of his movement plan. We can get an idea of the importance of the balancing rod's "availability" by trying to tread a narrow surface first with our arms out to the sides, then folded but unfastened behind our back so we can still use them to balance in an emergency. When we try the exercise again with our hands tied, either behind our back or in front of our body (here they're fastened with handcuffs in front), we are much more insecure.*

1 *The horse's amplitude of movement (extent or range of swing) can only swing through from the back to the front when the connection is not blocked due to misuse of the reins. The horse's poll should be the highest point and his nose should be just in front of the vertical.*

2 *When the horse is held tight and his nose is behind the vertical, his back will stiffen and will not be able to swing.*

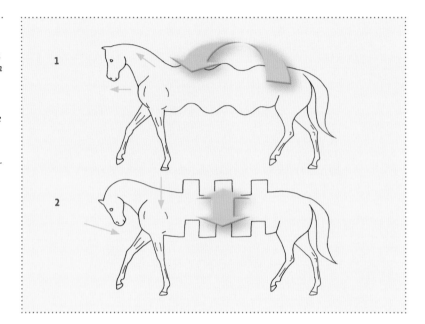

the withers as we discussed earlier (p. 96). When the horse's neck is shortened and his head is constrained behind the vertical, it leads unavoidably to a blockage in the movement of the lumbar area, which in turn negatively influences straightness, collection, the development of impulsion, throughness, and rhythm purity.

Uninterrupted, fluid motion

Straightness, engagement, and impulsion are the result of the natural movement of the horse being adjusted so there is an increased flexing of the haunches (akin to the "skiing" stance and flexion of the hips in humans). The flexing of the haunches makes it possible for the horse to turn relying on his hindquarters and without too much dependency on his "ski poles"—that is, the forehand. The Training Scale criteria are meant to test specifically for and to ensure the healthy fluid motion of the horse isn't interrupted.

    It is a high point for the rider when she is completely engaged in a dialogue of motion with the horse and experiences him when he is through, meaning that as her dance partner, he willingly takes her lead and smoothly puts her subtle requests into action.

The Instructor as a Translator in the Dialogue of Motion

Horses are less complicated than humans. They often can release stress, pain, or restriction immediately with a moment's relaxation. They don't "take things the wrong way" in a human sense, but react directly to whatever stimulates them.

When the rider can understand this and experience the dialogue she shares with the horse consciously and influence it, she learns what is known as "feel," which we've already discussed to some extent (p. 69). Her aim is to help the horse associate a body position under saddle with a feeling of well-being in motion, without being disturbed or stressed, and all the while enjoying his work.

My job as a riding teacher is to support both rider and horse in their motion dialogue so that they can accomplish together the

The horse notices when a third person, such as an instructor or trainer, supports him by correcting his rider when the rider interferes with his movement or bothers him. This develops a positive instructor-rider-horse relationship triangle.

increasingly difficult exercises with which they are challenged. To this end, I must form a relationship with both and—most importantly—help the rider learn to really feel the horse. Only then will she be open and receptive to the signals that the horse sends her.

In order for the horse to understand her, and for her to be helpful to the horse, the rider must do her part in the dialogue of motion by developing an independent seat and mastering how to give the aids. I work with all my students intensely and in detail on their seat, as well as how to consciously use motion impulses to make the horse's job easier. In this way, the rider and I further the horse's development together.

My riding student must learn to feel the signals the horse is giving her in order to better help him use his body optimally. No basic training is possible without suppleness and relaxation, contact that the horse confidently seeks by stretching to the bit, and a back that rhythmically swings from the hind end. This is the foundation that must be worked on at every phase of dressage training, up to Grand Prix.

From the first greeting at the beginning of a lesson, to the walk breaks and instructor-rider discussions, the horse indicates whether or not he feels himself to be a part of the relationship triangle.

The horse should sense that the rider helps him do what she asks of him in a manner that is comfortable to him. The horse can then participate joyfully and will strive to perform well since it makes him feel good to improve his ability to move.

Choose the classical way

The rider should be prepared to critically examine her own seat, body, motives, and rider attitude (meaning how she sees the horse and riding itself). She must especially consider the influence that she has on the horse. She needs to understand, internalize, and believe in the logic and system of classical training.

At the end of each training session the horse should be satisfied with himself and we should show him that we appreciate his participation.

It might not be easy to refuse to be led astray by the many know-it-alls who think that forcing the horse to yield to the hand in order to make him "rounder" is acceptable, or that riding the horse with a stiff back and fast tempo in order to make him look more "spectacular" is legitimate. Today there is the presumption that dressage riders can become successful much faster by riding in such a way.

As a riding instructor I have often seen my own students "stray" and attempt to try to achieve their riding goals in other ways. I can usually tell when this is the case in the first few minutes of a riding lesson—the horse's behavior, musculature, and motion show how he has been ridden since our last lesson together and whether the rider has drifted from correct training technique. It is usually easy to quickly repair the situation with just a few corrections.

But it is important that the rider experiences why the "other way" doesn't lead to the kind of improvement she expects or desires; she needs to feel for herself, through the horse's movement and the signals he sends, where the qualitative differences between classical training and modern methods are found. Usually, then the rider can resist future temptation and hold to the classical precepts with conviction.

The story of Dorien and Argentante

Dorien shares her story: "I came to Ulrike because I was desperate. My beautiful, beloved, and very nice-moving mare had been thrown out of the arena at almost all the shows I entered for being irregular. I knew that I got very anxious when I competed, but I didn't realize that

As a riding instructor, I encourage my students to stay on the horse-friendly path provided by the principles of classical training.

I was the cause of her "rein lameness." This lameness began to show up more frequently even though the veterinarians I consulted could not find a reason for it. Ulrike taught me that my riding and my own tension were the cause of Argentante's movement problems.

"I stopped riding at competitions, and instead we have worked on my seat and my communication with my horse from the saddle. As a result my mare and I are relaxing better and are adjusting to each other. After a while she stopped throwing her head, and I learned not to try to fix everything with my hands, which was only building tension in my horse.

"It is also noticeable that Argentante is more relaxed and trusts me more when riding outside the arena. I can even ride her at the head of a group, and she doesn't continually look back at the other horses or drag her feet, getting slower.

"After a few months of work with Ulrike, I rode as a demonstration rider at a symposium that Ulrike organized. I was able to ride in front of the audience without experiencing the kind of tension that had previously caused such problems at competitions. I noticed, however, that I still needed to work on riding in front of people, because in public I don't perform as well as I do at home or in my regular lessons with Ulrike."

Dorien's father, who follows the lessons and his daughter's training at home says, "It is wonderful to see how Dorien and Argentante are building more trust in each other. The problems that seemed to be escalating for so long are now gone."

My work with Dorien and Argentante

Dorien is getting more secure, due to much of the work she does with her mare in the time between lessons, and she has her own body and head under better control. Now and then I can tell that she hasn't controlled the tempo well or that her horse has been ridden too much on the forehand, but that is easily corrected. Dorien is learning to gauge the correctness of her riding and make adjustments herself when things go too much in one direction or another.

We still have to work on the competition aspect because Dorien puts a lot of pressure on herself and gets unnecessarily tense, but I know we will also get that under control. That is something that we have to work on in Dorien's head. When Dorien feels good enough about her work with Argentante, then she won't let an audience distract her. She must stay focused and practice continuing to ride in a dialogue with the horse even while under stress. When she can do that, she can participate happily in competitions again. She will surely be successful since her mare moves very well and is being trained correctly.

Dorien and Argentante.

Backslide: The "through the poll" trap

Once, at the beginning of a lesson, I noticed immediately that Argentante was going behind the vertical with a short and braced neck. Her muscling hadn't continued to develop as I expected, and Dorien held her hands deep and pressed on the reins. As we talked, it came out that at her riding club where she took lessons, she had been told to "make the horse give better" and to "ride her more through the poll." She was also supposed to ride more forward. Due to the short neck and the forced "contact" at a tempo that was too fast, her horse's back was now too tense to work correctly and her hind legs were trailing out in back.

We spent a quarter of an hour helping Dorien find a good feel again. From this experience, Dorien learned to not be influenced by such advice. She is learning to trust her own feel more. That is an important step toward competing again.

Unfortunately, today's riding instructors and judges expect us to ride our horse more "through the poll"—meaning to hold the horse in a "rounder" position with the hands. Judges often give higher

Here Dorien is posting too high at the trot, which causes her horse to come onto the forehand.

points for a forced contact and don't appear to understand the horse's biomechanics.

It isn't easy for riders to find their way in today's horse world. As an instructor and trainer I must try to make it clear to the rider how movement should feel and look when the horse is happy and ridden in a way that is anatomically and biomechanically correct. When the rider experiences that herself and can internalize it, then she can resist all kinds of external temptation. She can continue training with the reward being the positive development of the horse and harmony in their partnership, rather than in collecting ribbons and trophies in competition.

It is normal for a young horse to look around and to use his neck to balance himself, as we've discussed. When he stays tuned in to the rider, on her aids, and continues forward, movement of the neck in this way isn't bad. Restricting him with the hands is the worst thing we can do.

As soon as the rider gets tense or starts pulling, it is a signal for the horse to get tense, and eventually, to try to escape the pressure or just stop. The horse comes "against the rein" when his movement has been interrupted by the rider's hands like this. The blockage can be dissolved quickly when the rider corrects herself by "giving" the inside rein with independent, sensitive hands, while keeping the hindquarters active and maintaining the horse's back activity with her seat and legs. The horse then relaxes the musculature under his neck and seeks the contact again confidently. The hindquarters and forehand are reconnected through a back that is relaxed and arched.

Before the horse can be corrected, the seat of the rider must be improved.

When Dorien can develop this feeling of connection with ever lighter aids—and without working from front to back against the motion—then Argentante will be better gymnasticized. Dorien will be able to tell when she is doing well when Argentante has a better developed upper-neck musculature, a clearly more relaxed long back muscle that moves up and down behind the saddle, and a general expression of contented and comfortable movement through her whole body. She will gain confidence in how to support her mare and the trust between them will grow rapidly. In the foreseeable future we will be able to prepare the pair for a competition without causing them stress.

1 To recover her balance, Argentante shakes her head, becomes irregular and tries to get loose.

2 Argentante reacts with tension to the tension of her rider.

3 Dorien must have independent, raised hands to enable her to sit up straight. She must maintain a relaxed contact with the horse's mouth. In this way the bit is simply a medium of communication and doesn't disturb the horse's motion.

4 Dorien's legs need to hang loose from her hips and "hug" the horse to ensure suppleness in Argentante's body and movement flowing over her back. They also enable Dorien to help her horse step further under her body with her hind legs.

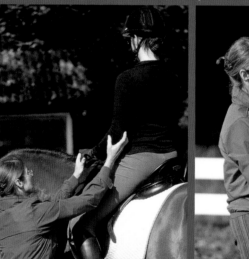

5–6 When Dorien manages to stay relaxed, Argentante drops her head. Now Dorien must activate her horse from behind and motivate her to stretch to the bit.

7

8

7 *Now Dorien can ask Argentante to step with more activity on a volte by bringing her inside hind leg diagonally under her body without speeding up. Argentante begins to move uphill, engage a little, and straighten.*

8 *The voltes become easier for Argentante; Dorien must always work on maintaining the correct seat in turns.*

9

10

9 *It is easier for Dorien to ride the turns from her seat at the canter and engage Argentante. She makes sure her horse "jumps through," the movement coming powerfully over the arched back and upper neck.*

10 *Then Dorien brings her horse's hindquarters a little more under her. We see how Argentante is more "put together" and cantering quietly uphill. By changing between a stretching position and being "put together," Dorien learns to control her mare and teaches her to move from her hind end.*

11

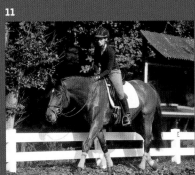

11 *At the end of the session, both rider and horse are pleased to have come a step further in their work together. We can tell that the work was good by the way the horse walks easily, relaxed on a long rein. Both can now store this positive learning experience in their mind and muscle memory.*

Els and her Belgian Warmblood Ben.

The story of Els and Ben

Els shares her story: "Ben is a Belgian Warmblood out of the Donner-hall line (Dodewaart). I rode him as a three-year-old in several stallion tests. He got excited easily and was very 'looky.' This often led to him throwing his head up and becoming unrideable. I frequently couldn't circle him to the left.

"Two years ago I took lessons on developing my seat from Ulrike on her school horses. I have my own boarding barn, give riding lessons, and start young horses. My own seat has suffered a lot from that.

I really wanted to ride Ben in dressage competitions, but it became clear quickly that it wasn't going to be possible with the seat I had: I had trouble keeping my legs quiet and controlling my hands. However, as my seat improved during longeing lessons on Ulrike's school horses, and I saw the benefit at home riding my own horses and in giving lessons, I asked Ulrike to help me with the particular problems I had with Ben. She helped me for a half a year.

"I had to reduce the tempo of the gaits, concentrate above all on my seat and my hands, and not try to 'ride him under' with my hands any more. Ben became much more relaxed, and I could better straighten and control him. We progressed well in basic training. Ben moved over the back and got stronger and more elastic. Unfortunately, I stopped taking lessons for a while due to time constraints. I gelded Ben and just rode him at my local riding club.

Backslide: the too-fast tempo

"It wasn't long before I started riding him at a too-fast tempo, too 'forward' again, while forcing him to yield to my hands. In a very short time Ben was no longer reasonable to ride. He again kept his head high and spooked at everything. His steps were short and frenzied, and in very little time he had developed enormous muscling on the underside of his neck. His whole musculature changed and was incorrect. That alarmed me.

"I noticed also that my seat had gotten bad again when riding my other horses, so I restarted regular lessons with Ulrike. First I came with Ben. Ulrike saw immediately what was wrong and put me on the longe line for several sessions. Then she worked with Ben and me. It wasn't long before I started finding my seat again, and Ben started to feel the way I remembered him before.

"We are now improving together once again. I have learned to not get frustrated when he looks around at the beginning of a lesson and lifts his head. I don't start correcting him right away with my hands. I provide better security and support with my seat. Naturally, we both have a lot more to learn, but it is going better, and I can tell that we keep improving steadily.

At the beginning of our lesson, I have to work with Els and Ben on becoming supple and relaxed together on the circle.

"Above all, I have learned through these experiences with Ben that I won't turn away from the classical path again. It seems to take more effort to concentrate so intensely on communication rather than to force the horse into a posture and 'step on the gas,' but the fantastic feeling that we get when the horse relaxes and enjoys participating is incomparable. Ben is happy after every lesson; he's learned something and tries hard to do it right. He is starting to show his naturally large and beautiful motion. He doesn't move with 'spectacular' action, but round and with lightness. That makes us both happy."

My work with Els and Ben

After it became easier for Els and Ben to achieve suppleness and relaxation, I worked with them on developing engagement, meaning the horse's acceptance of more weight on his hindquarters. We worked on

straightening Ben through many voltes and turns to make him equal-
ly strong and elastic in both directions. We also included transitions,
corrrectly supporting him with the seat in school figures, and cavalletti. With dressage cavalletti work, I can encourage the rider's ability
to feel when the horse is supporting himself well from the hind legs
and over the back, as well as nurture a sensitive development of connection with the horse.

   I work on both of them, in order to bring them both farther along.
Ben now relaxes his back more easily and starts stretching on
straightaways, almost by himself. Els now understands how easily
the rider can positively or negatively influence the horse and works
very diligently on herself. She achieves a lot—not only with Ben, but
also with her other horses.

Here we see Els as she supports Ben with her seat to provide security, slow the tempo, and help him to find balance in the turn.

1 At the beginning of a lesson, Ben is usually excited and maintains a flight animal's alertness in order to be able to "run away from danger."

2 Els must not get irritated or angry with this behavior, or try to control it with strong hands and a tempo that is too fast.

3 Els supports Ben with her seat to give him a sense of security. She slows the tempo and helps him to find his balance through suppleness and relaxation. In this way, Ben learns to find his balance using his hind end and coming over the back and not by running away with a hollow back.

4 When Ben gets fast or "looky," Els must not try to solve the problem with her hands.

5 As we can see, her hands do not try to force her horse to yield with pressure.

6 Finally, Ben can relax the muscles under his neck and stretch to the bit. The wither vertebrae "fan" open, and he can relax his back.

7

8

7 As soon as Ben lets the neck fall and "opens" at the withers, his back relaxes, his upper neck firms up from connection to the active hindquarters, and he straightens and can move with more engagement.

8 Els can only do well as long as the muscles on the underside of Ben's neck stay relaxed and the tempo doesn't get too fast.

9

10

9 Above all, dressage must evolve from a "posture of well-being"—one that is good for the horse. When this is lost, it must be reestablished at a quiet walk.

10 Els must be prepared for when Ben spooks, gets too fast, or "puffs up" with growing tension.

11

12

11 She must relax her inside (inside the bend) hand, relax Ben with her seat, and ride at a quiet rate of rhythm on a circle. She must never try to control him with her hands.

12 Calm, active, but relaxed trotting in a stretching frame with the horse's nose in front of the vertical (but without going on the forehand) is a reasonable option when reestablishing control, but is especially useful at the end of the lesson. This exercise provides optimal regeneration as a cool-down.

Questionable Training Methods

In many of today's "modern training methods" it is postulated that gymnasticization of the horse through extreme flexion or hyperflexion of the neck leads to the horse moving better with more throughness. This goal is pursued by putting the horse's body into positions that are consciously omitted from the classical teachings, including severe sideways flexion of the neck, overflexion of the neck in a "rolled up" position, or riding exercises on two tracks at a high speed. Through these extremes in position and tempo the horse will supposedly become more athletic and blockages will be worked out. Proponents argue that the classical school is limited in its use of only very specific positions. Herein lies a huge misunderstanding. The classical masters knew only too well why we should limit variations in the horse's position and tempo to those that align with his biomechanics and well-being. They intentionally excluded combinations of posture, movement, and tempo that were not physically or psychologically beneficial to the horse. Naturally, a classically trained rider doesn't always succeed in reaching the ideal, but such deviations from the ideal occur due to inability rather than intention.

When we analyze questionable postures and incorrect riding according to the criteria of the Training Scale, most are immediately identifiable as being bad for the horse since they lead to at least one criterion of the scale not being fulfilled. In effect, they disturb the flow of motion through his body and his general well-being.

Flexion and Hyperflexion

The term flexion comes from *inflexus*, the Latin word for bending. Hyperflexion means extreme bending of one or several joints, which can lead to these joints being damaged. Hyperflexion in the horse is also known as the "rollkur" training method: the horse's neck is intentionally shortened and overflexed between the second and fourth neck vertebrae. Additionally, the horse is positioned or flexed extremely to the side. Tendons, muscle groups, and ligaments are overstretched in this practice.

Recap: Rider Errors

Let's take another look at how rider errors disturb the flow of motion

Common Riding Errors and Their Impact

Here I demonstrate the most common rider errors that negatively influence fluidity in the horse's motion and which are unpleasant or even painful to him. They also negatively affect the horse's mental well-being. All these errors lead to a blockage in the lumbar area, which hinders the horse's ability to move according to the Training Scale criteria.

It's always a little uncomfortable to intentionally ride my horse incorrectly in order to show my students something. Due to my horse Hans' physical predisposition, it is easy to trigger a blockage in the lumbar area, but due to his classical training, it is also quick to work it out again. For the most part, it only took about a half of a circle of demonstrating an error to produce each situation shown.

Here we can see how the lumbar area is "blocked" by the horse's shortened the neck and "absolute elevation" (the horse's head-neck axis is positioned higher and compressed beyond the level of the horse's training). My position disturbs the activity of the horse's back by leaning back.

Thanks for helping, Hans!

The fluidity of the horse's movement is interrupted when rollkur and hyperflexion (extreme positioning or bending of the neck) is used. I am leaning back and to the inside. Note how the horse's inside hind leg can't step under anymore.

Absolute elevation ridden from the rider's hands is just as damaging as Rollkur. The neck is shortened, and the back is tense and pushed up. The blockage in the lumbar area is distinctly visible.

A true stretching frame is not possible when the position is forced by the rider's hands (my hands are wide and pressing down). The horse has to curl his neck, he goes on the forehand, and his lumbar region is blocked.

I have interrupted Hans' flow of motion by extremely shortening and curling his neck. His back activity is blocked, and he can't move freely forward out of his shoulders.

Hans' nose is pulled in to his chest, and I am stiff and leaning back. Hans' forehand is clearly overloaded and his tail shows his tension.

Hans' neck and poll are held too tightly and the position hurts him. He is on the forehand and his back is tight, which makes it hard for me to sit. At the moment, his outside front leg is extremely overloaded on a turn. There is no flexing of the haunches on his right side since the joints must stay straight due to the blockage in his lumbar region.

and the well-being of the horse. Frequent mistakes are:
- Shortening the horse's frame.
- Providing "no frame" (riding without contact).
- Blocking from the seat (not sitting straight, collapsing sideways).
- Blocking from the leg (constantly clutching or thumping).
- Overflexing the neck and positioning it to one side.
- Overflexing the neck by "rolling" or "curling" it in or by shortening it.

Correcting Hans' carriage: Here he stretches again to the bit and moves at the correct tempo with free, swinging back activity.

Learning to Read the Horse's Body Language

Many riders unfortunately have little opportunity to experience the horse moving at liberty in a natural setting. The same goes for seeing the horse engaged in correct and expressive motion while under saddle. Unfortunately, the average rider who begins taking lessons at a riding stable doesn't get to see many horses moving happily and harmoniously under their rider—she mostly sees school horses that have to cope with the inabilities of the rider in training. It seems today that few riders have the chance to watch horses associate in a herd so as to get a glimpse "inside" a contented horse and see how he expresses himself in his behavior. And in terms of watching happy horses under saddle, even at the highest levels of dressage we see images that are far from harmonious.

Since my horses live in a group and can move and express themselves freely, I can learn a lot from watching them and seeing how they are doing on any given day. I always keep an eye on the following, for example:

- After working, how does the horse go back to the pasture or paddock? Is he tired, excited, or under pressure? Does he seem to need to "decompress" after a training session through free movement or

During a walk on a long rein Hans shows that all is in order again, despite having to deal with my staged incorrect riding. Hans is walking again with a relaxed back. His hips move back and forth, his hind legs step under. He feels good again, drops his neck, stretches, and is content.

aggression toward other horses? Does he pull back from his pasture mates or seek contact?

· Does the horse willingly let himself be caught when it is time for a training session? Does he come up to me, stand waiting for me to approach, or otherwise show me through hesitation or turning away that he actually doesn't want to participate?

· How does he stand before and after training in the aisle or wash stall?

· Does his normal behavior change when turned out in the group? Sometimes I have to take these signals into consideration and adjust the training plan.

Having his balance disrupted is stressful to the horse

Even the highly trained horse that has learned to accept his rider still has his natural instincts. In a flight animal, this means that panic can erupt every now and then. The more tuned in the horse is to the rider and vice versa, and the more the rider can communicate with precision, the more she is in a position to reassure the horse and keep him from panicking.

Now and then the rider herself can trigger the "Help! Predator!" instinct. For example, when she hurts the horse or gets him out of balance, he can feel much like a tennis player who is standing on the wrong foot when hitting the ball—he can't run. Such a feeling causes discomfort and even stress in a flight animal.

On the other hand, when the horse experiences the rider as someone who tries to help him by being in balance with him, he is ready to do extraordinary things in order to accomplish a common goal. For example, I have seen horses save themselves and their rider when caught in what could have been disastrous situations on the jump course.

In classical riding, we take these considerations into account by defining the position and aids of the rider so that she neither disturbs the horse nor causes him pain. We bring the horse in motion into body positions that help him find his balance, and which the horse then associates with comfort. When the horse falls into or is put into a position that doesn't feel naturally balanced, it causes him physical and mental stress. Other such causes of stress are when he is forced

Here my hands are very wide and pulling up. As a result, Hans' right hind leg steps sideways and not under his center of gravity as is desirable. His back activity is blocked and he is no longer balanced.

When I rely on my hands and leaning back to come to a halt, I cause a blockage in my horse's lumbar region as the muscles on the underside of his neck brace. The horse stops out of balance, with his hind legs trailing.

into a body position where he can't carry the rider without strain and when he isn't allowed to maintain his balance as may be necessary.

Example: the effect of the dropped back

The effect of a dropped back on the psychology of the horse illustrates quite clearly the connection between psychological and physical stress. When a horse sees something that might be dangerous—for example, a tractor when out riding in the countryside—he naturally reacts with a dropped back, raised head, and tensed muscles on the underside of his neck. The dropped back is closely associated in the nervous system with mobilization of a panic response. The horse prepares to run away in fear that is expressed both physically and mentally.

When a rider works a horse a long time with a dropped back because the rider sits poorly, disturbs the horse's mouth, the saddle doesn't fit, or for any number of other reasons, it results in back pain and wear and tear in the horse, as well as permanent psychological stress. The horse is actually being ridden in a constant state of psychological alarm therefore is not able to relax physically or mentally, since this body position is associated with his instinctual flight behavior. Consequently, the horse can't concentrate on his rider and learn well. Learning, as we have seen already in this book, must always be connected with positive feelings in order to be successful.

When the rider doesn't succeed in stopping the cause of the dropped back, then the horse continues to tense up. Soon he can't travel any more in a pure rhythm, and this disturbs his balance. A vicious cycle develops that is difficult to break.

When a horse is ridden with a back that is dropped for long periods, he experiences both physical and psychological stress.

Stress

The word stress comes from the Latin *strictus*, which can be translated as tense or tight. The Austrian-Canadian physician Hans Selye (1907–1982) took the word stress from physics (material science), where it signifies traction or pressure applied to a substance, and adapted the term to the vocabularies of medicine and psychology. Stress is understood to be the physical/emotional condition where one subjectively feels overwhelmed. There is a dysfunctional mobilization of reserves without the ability to overcome the challenge. In contrast to a measured training load, stress doesn't result in adaptation or supercompensation (see p. 92), but rather sensitization. Consequently, a stress trigger results in a stress overreaction. In humans, such an oversensitization can lead to post-traumatic stress disorder (PTSD).

Arousal level, pressure, fear, and stress

The word stress is used with various meanings. Feeling "stressed" is frequently associated with having too much to do despite not being lazy. The original meaning of the word, however, is not positive for man or animal. When speaking of stress in equine sports, cause and effect are frequently confused.

When the activation level (energy level experienced in body and mind prior to performance, ranging from deep sleep to extreme excitement) increases to that of stress, fear, or panic, then the individual is no longer capable of emotionally/physically processing the situation.

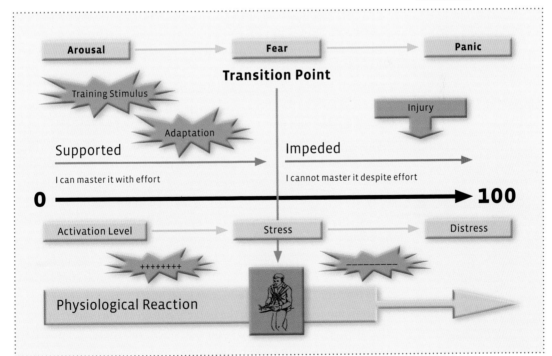

When a horse is anxious and tense when receiving ribbons and prizes, even after years of winning and standing in the spotlight, he probably suffers from stress sensitization.

This horse's facial expression and rigid musculature show that he is under stress.

Frequently, activation level—the energy level experienced in body and mind prior to performance, ranging from deep sleep to extreme excitement—and stress are equated. Some argue that stress in training increases stamina in competitions. That doesn't make sense. The pressure of training should never result in stress. Just as we can't learn when afraid, the body can't become more fit under stress.

As is shown in the illustration on p. 163, a raised activation level as a psychological and physiological response to mind-body performance remains productive only as long as it doesn't evolve into stress or panic. When a certain point is exceeded, the otherwise useful physiological activation process has the opposite effect and not only massively hinders the mind-body activity but can injure the individual.

Consequently, it is illogical to speak of positive eustress (said to be the positive response one has to a stressor—for example, seeing it as a challenge instead of a threat) and negative distress (the negative response when one cannot adapt to a stressor). As soon as there is a stress reaction, a positive productive level of activation is exceeded. The individual—in this case the horse—engages in negative coping behaviors, namely stress and panic reactions, and these are apparent in both his appearance and behavior.

Body postures can become stressors that the horse associates with fear, pain, confinement, and the inability to flee (very stressful to a flight animal). The rider herself can become a stressor when she rides like a predator on the horse's back.

Signs of physical stress

The tension, readiness to flee, and stress that a horse feels can be seen in visible body signals. His breathing can become irregular. The horse sometimes hyperventilates. His eye movement increases; the whites are visible. His ears move nervously, and as they move back and forth, they don't appear friendly and open to the rider and the surroundings, but instead signal that the horse would like to escape. The horse sweats even when not engaged in strenuous activity. His tail switches with great irritation. The horse's movement in general is certainly active, but it is not harmonious or fluid. His movements aren't round but come in a frenetic series, which sometimes today is described as "electric" as if they are exciting to watch.

When we are familiar with the demeanor of a comfortable horse

This horse shows us that his back hurts with an obviously switching tail.

This horse shows the stress-induced sweat pattern typical of a horse that is physically and emotionally overwhelmed.

The expression of a stressed and overwhelmed horse after completing a test.

that is attentive, active, and confident, then we can also recognize the look that signals "I am irritated" or "I am about to panic." Stress can lead to kicking, bucking, and flight reactions or to the horse standing stiff as a board. A physiologist measuring the horse's heartbeat would typically find a permanently raised heart rate. This is part of the stress reaction that causes the flight response.

The impact over time of such stress on the horse depends on his individual physical and emotional development and constitution. Some horses (mostly natural herd leaders) protest, others become very insecure, and still others endure their lot like an abused child, their body moving and continuing on like an empty shell but with the inner self not really "present." These reactions can continue on until they result in physical damage—as is now known, stomach ulcers are not uncommon in these horses.

Example: the effect of horse show anxiety

When a rider forces movement, is stiff in the saddle, or is stressed and tense herself, the horse can instinctively perceive this and sees it as (respectively) a predator's aggression or an insecure herdmate's readiness to flee. Insecurity and tension in the rider affect the horse's physical and emotional well-being and have visible consequences. When the rider causes the horse pain or hinders his movement, then physical and psychological mechanisms are triggered that impede a harmonious dialogue of motion between them. This is clearly reflected in the physical demeanor of the horse.

Many riders with horse show anxiety know this phenomenon well. They either have an extremely strong desire to ride well, and therefore are "too busy" in the saddle, or they become tense as a result of their own nervousness and don't communicate the aids well. The horse mirrors this behavior in his motion and expression. He becomes fearful, "disobedient," moves frenetically, or completely refuses to perform. When the rider manages to get her own tension under control, the horse also relaxes, looks content, and this shows in his beautiful, fluid motion.

Achieving relaxation through body position adjustments

It is true that we can use adjustments to the horse's body posture to

make work easier for him and his rider in certain situations. If we put
an excited horse that is distracted by his rider a little (note emphasis
on a little) rounder and deeper for a short time, ride a volte,
and support him in a rhythmical, swinging, relaxed forward motion,
he will lighten, arch his back, and "find his mind" again through
the motion. When he is again relaxed and attentive, normal training
can resume.

My diagonal aids (lateral aids are on one side of the horse, while diagonal aids work on both sides—for example, inside rein and outside leg) allow my horse to stretch to the bit through the outside (of the bend), while the bend instigated by the placement of his inside hind leg goes through his whole body. His inside hip lowers, and I practically "turn him on the inside hind leg" through his outside shoulder. I sit over the horse's center of gravity (I don't lean to the inside and back on the curve). My position enables my horse to perform the turn on his hindquarters.

Learned Helplessness

Learned Helplessness

The term learned helplessness comes from an extension of stimulus-response studies on depression performed by the American psychologist Martin Seligman. It refers to the mental state or condition when an animal has experienced a series of negative or painful stimuli from which it can't escape. Eventually, the animal stops trying to avoid the unpleasantness or pain as a result of a perceived lack of control over the situation—it feels helpless. This state can expand to apply to other scenarios, where the animal doesn't defend itself, even in situations where it can.

When the horse is forced in this way, something is wrong with the way he is being ridden.

As we have discussed, in contrast to the classical, horse-friendly way of training horses, today there are other methods that do not grant "partner status" to the horse, but rather degrade him to little more than a "black box" required to react at the press of a button. Trained in this way, the horse reaches a state of learned helplessness. He is at the mercy of his rider because she doesn't react to any of the horse's attempts to enter into a dialogue with her. He learns that he can't escape and therefore capitulates. Since horses are flight animals and are highly mobile, their movements in such scenarios is hyperactive, which may look "spectacular," but they have been achieved via a military dialogue where an order given should be obeyed (see p. 55). There is no concern about the effect of long-lasting stress on the horse, because the stress is intentionally created.

Increasing the activation level by increasing control

By forcing a horse into unnatural body postures and motion patterns, the horse can turn into what is essentially a highly functional "stress bundle" that reacts hyperactively. Under extreme conditions he simply psychologically "tunes out" while continuing to function physically in what some deem a "spectacular" way. Certain techniques, auxiliary equipment such as draw reins, or incorrectly used curb bits are used to keep him under control.

Almost every experienced rider knows how she can get her horse "revved up" or excited. By giving contradictory aids, for example, a horse can go very quickly to a rather high level of activation (see p. 163). Trust between riding partners suffers, but the horse's movements can become spectacular as a result. When we look closely, we can see in the expression of the horse that his actions have been bought with stress. His eyes, facial expression, breathing pattern, and general body tension reveal the trick.

The horse reacts in the same way to being ridden in extreme positions for a long period of time, for example, with his nose to his chest. His balance is massively disturbed, as the natural balancing rod, the neck, is disabled. In addition, the horse cannot see where he is going. These are all conditions that cause psychological stress in a flight animal. When we add pain in the mouth, jaw, and poll from the effect of incorrectly applied curb bits and the use of draw reins, then a panic level is reached and the horse reacts extremely.

Usually the horse learns that the rider is not prepared to react to his signals of distress. He must continue on regardless of whether or not he is physically balanced and whether he can see or not. He must keep working although he can't move his head or neck himself. When we consider the fact that a horse can be held to the ground by just the neck (as when a predator attacks), then we can well imagine the instinctive reaction in the mind of the horse. In moments like this, the rider controls the horse just like a predator holds him on the ground. Protest of the position is either no longer possible or can occur only via the extreme effort.

Further troublesome practices include the rider pulling the horse to a halt and immediately digging in her spurs. Then, as the horse jumps away from the pressure from the spurs, the rider stands in the stirrups and pulls on the reins. Believe me, it's all been done. The horse learns over and over that he must react only with extreme movements of the legs, which he does. He does it because "not reacting" results in more stress. Hot-blooded horses that are

Added to the physical pain he experiences in the mouth, poll, back, and lumbar region is the psychological stress that arises when the horse's cry for help goes unheeded.

This horse has clearly exerted a lot of energy in the test he just finished, but is just as clearly relaxed and "pleased with himself."

temperamental and hyperactive are most likely to accept this reaction pattern and the stress that goes with it, at least for a while, and give the desired extra "show" to their movements. Others are not so likely to comply. At the top of dressage sport today we mainly see those that can at least temporarily cope.

Abused children?

As we've touched upon, the horse is made helpless through such training practices. He is like an abused child that knows that something isn't right, but has to do what he is told anyway. For those that indulge in such training methods, they are lucky if they have a very active and highly functional horse for a period of time that can also be controlled. However, just like the abused child, damage shows up at some point down the road. Many horses in these situations refuse or rebel at some time because they physically or mentally just can't do it anymore.

"Abnormal" behavior after a test or training session

The "modern" training methods such as we've discussed in this book provide effective control. The price paid for such control, especially by the horse, is unfortunately very high. We can see in the whole way the horse moves that he is tense, and this tension doesn't ease when the reins are long and the test or training session is over. Sometimes it is almost disturbingly comical to hear enthusiastic applause from the crowd and at the same time see in the arena or exit area a stressed horse with fearful eyes that desperately tries to save himself in motion (via flight).

Even when not applying incorrect and damaging training methods, rider errors can lead to short and ever-lengthening periods of broken communication where the horse can react to her requests with irritation. The horse in this case, however, at least isn't stuck in a permanent state of psychological insecurity.

Horses that are made insecure systematically show their tension in their behavior not only during but also after a test or training session. Frequently, this behavior is misinterpreted as evidence of a bad temperament. For example, the horse jumps away when the rider goes to get back on after the award ceremony. He continues to piaffe or passage, even when the test is long finished. Breathing, sweating, rolling his eyes, and flicking his ears nervously—such expressions show a very insecure and frightened horse, rather than the horse that is satisfied with his performance, still active, but relaxed, and that has enjoyed the interaction with his rider. Unfortunately many novices believe that this stress behavior is "normal" horse behavior and that this is how a sport horse today should behave.

In my youth I watched the training at the Spanish Riding School in Vienna several times a week and saw how the horses were animated to the highest level of performance. But I always saw content, quiet horses that could immediately find their inner balance again after a powerful high school jump, and they could always confidently step forward to receive reward or accolades.

Insecure horses show their tension after a dressage test, as well as during it.

Even when the test is over, the stressed horse stays hyperactive and passages on and on and on...

Ridden: Classical or Push-Button?

Respect for the Horse as Our Partner

Since the horse is a social herd animal, he is astoundingly willing to
do what humans ask of him despite the power they can exert over
him. Anyone who has started a young horse under saddle in a humane
and responsible way knows how surprisingly fast the horse willingly
figures out what is wanted of him. Over the centuries, people have
respected this phenomenon. The original "Directives of the Spanish
Riding School" are a beautiful example.

The difference between classical training and the training methods that have been gaining ever more ground in recent years in international dressage—known as Rollkur, "Hyperflexion," "New Dutch
School," or "modern dressage"—lies in how we communicate with
the horse. In classical training, the horse and rider communicate like
two dance partners through intuitively understandable movement

*In classical riding the horse's
body posture fits the movement
pattern.*

impulses and signals—the rider "leads" and supports the horse in his formation of a movement plan and his execution of it. This is a very different principle from today's methods where the horse is just "programmed" to provide certain reactions. He learns to respond to certain stimuli or secondary aids (see p. 64) that make no intrinsic sense to him—in other words, he performs at the push of a button rather than engages in a conversation.

After all we have said in this book about the mind-body aspects of reactive versus planned movement and the psychological results of the human riding in the form of a predator, it is clear that this type of push-button obedience is accomplished only by causing the horse fear and stress.

Nevertheless, riding that uses stimulus-response learning (see p. 45 for our discussion of this concept), in all its various forms, continues to gain traction and establish itself under all kinds of tag lines—sometimes even with claims of being horse-friendly.

Intentional Use of the "Predator Principle"

When we compare classical, horse-friendly riding with stimulus-response riding as practiced in the new "modern" school of dressage training, it is clear that they are two completely different approaches.

In correct classical riding we only work in body postures that fit the current movement pattern, allowing the horse the ability to temporarily give up the contact to rebalance himself as needed. The rider teaches the horse that she is interested in his well-being and isn't a predator that wants to use force to unbalance him. She tries to keep the "Help! Predator!" instinct at bay, since it leads to stress, unnecessary tension, and unhealthy reactions in the horse.

With stimulus-response-based riding, the rider intentionally behaves as a controlling predator who continually unbalances the horse in order to show him that she is the one who has the power, and what she says, goes. As I've stated before, there is no concern for the stress that develops in the horse because it is intentional. The horse's movement becomes frenetic and so he exhibits more active, spectacu-

These illustrations depict variations in posture and movement that are not classically correct for the horse.

This is a dysfunctional body posture and movement pattern in the horse. This combination leads to increased anxiety.

lar strides, which are really nothing more than an activated stress reaction in a desperate desire to run away.

Reactive movement without forewarning

Since the stimulus-response-based rider has an absolute need to control and doesn't want the horse to think along with her, she stops the horse's ability to plan his movement intentionally. She forces him to quickly react to secondary aids, instead. While the classically trained rider uses half-halts to help the horse stay in balance or get back in balance, and prepare him for the next movement, the push-button rider avoids half-halts completely. She doesn't warn the horse before she provokes the next reaction. This makes movement planning impossible for the horse.

Stimulus-response-based riding with the horse forced to react without being able to plan his movement.

Although this horse is very restricted by the rider's hands and body, he is driven by her seat and leg to shoot forward like he's coming out of a cannon. The criteria of the Training Scale and the horse's well-being fall by the wayside in an effort to achieve spectacular movement.

When the horse no longer can see where he is going, the rider becomes, in effect, his "seeing-eye dog," except in the case of modern training techniques, she doesn't lead him but only further undermines his ability to form a movement plan.

Deliberate fixation and pain

Deliberate fixation of the horse in unnatural body postures is part and parcel of the stimulus-response and push-button reaction theories. As we now know, this prevents reasonable actions by the horse, such as balancing with the neck when necessary. The horse is intentionally forced into reactive movement patterns that are not only uncomfortable for him but damaging to his health over time. There is no regard for the purpose and intent of classical training, which is to improve the horse and make him more beautiful. The goal of this training method isn't the development of self-confidence, but rather total dependence and learned helplessness (see p. 168).

Such forcefulness doesn't spare the physical integrity of the horse. Breathing is more difficult because the neck is rolled in and the nose is pulled behind the vertical toward the horse's chest. The horse gets less air while great physical exertion is demanded of him. His sight is almost completely taken from him—his view is restricted to the ground. He is forced to move forward, unbalanced, into "Nothingness." Since he doesn't trust his rider but fears her (she's a predator who will likely cause him to lose his balance again), he is practically always in a state of blind flight.

A marionette instead of a ballet dancer

As we saw in our earlier discussion on learned helplessness, stimulus-response-based riding reaches a state where the horse is conditioned to be hyperactive and "electric" in response to secondary aids (see p. 64). The horse holds his back so tightly that his front legs fly unnaturally high. The blockage in the lumbar vertebrae prevents him from carrying his weight more on the hindquarters as he should in dressage. In this state, the horse is like a marionette that pulls his legs up high when the rider pulls a string. His steps are stiff and stabbing since his joints can't provide shock absorption. His haunches don't flex and his back doesn't arch to dampen the impact.

The advocates of this method say that a "new type of motion" is created from "positive tension." We should reflect on this, since the Training Scale never mentions positive tension.

How to turn a horse into a marionette

In order to control the horse like we would a marionette, he is subjected to a series of massive and non-stop negative stimuli from which he cannot escape. The rider continually gives the horse signals that prevent any initiative of his own—for example, pulling on his mouth as soon as he speeds up in response to cues to increase his speed. Many riders use their legs and pull on the reins almost at the same time, while leaning back and hanging with the upper body behind the vertical and clamping with their thighs.

The rider disregards the biomechanical and mind-body principles of an independent seat and willingly accepts the resulting negative impact on the horse. She pulls his head to the side to "flex" him and doesn't react to the signals that the horse sends that say something like, "I am no longer balanced. I have enough to do just stepping under my center of gravity, which by the way, we are constantly changing. How can I now go any faster? Additionally, my mouth hurts, my tongue is clamped down, I can't breathe and can't see where I am going. Please give a little so that I can breathe again and so my mouth won't hurt so much and the pain in my back and poll can finally stop!"

Nevertheless, the rider drives the horse more forward with spurs, even when the horse starts hopping with both hind legs like a rabbit

1 *This horse is active but helpless and under stress.*

2 *He sweats to the extreme in the loin area.*

1

2

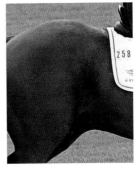

Muscle tension and a mouth agape in pain show that this horse doesn't feel good—but to many, his discomfort is considered acceptable.

trying to save himself from his predicament. Proponents argue that reaction and control are actually more important than the rhythm and purity of the gaits.

It is happening everywhere

Dressage is not alone in use of these methods. Jumper riders and drivers, Western and gaited breed riders—those who swear by this method come from all disciplines and levels, and they all claim their horses simply work better and are more controllable when trained with these techniques.

I find it terrible that this method has been consciously promulgated as "effective" by some riders and trainers at the top of the sport and that it has been rewarded in medals.

Over the last several years, I have analyzed more than 10 hours of video of riders using the hyperflexion method. The rolling or curling of the neck so the nose meets the chest is one of the characteristics, but not the only one. The horse is also almost always unbalanced, held tight in the front, and jabbed from behind with the spurs.

These horses show many indications in their physical expression of their deep psychological and physical insecurity. We can see that they aren't fully "present" any more—they "check out." They wall themselves off from the outside although they are overstimulated.

We can see the similar reactions in many riding school horses and also in privately owned horses. It is a problem that runs across the whole bandwidth—although mostly these are a result of rider errors and not due to the intentional use of uncomfortable stimuli.

Controlling techniques are also used among jumper riders, even though it actually discourages the bascule required for jumping well.

1

1–2 We also see these methods in gaited horses, such as Icelandics, and in Western riding events.

2

An Interview with Christine Stückelberger and Georg Wahl

How do you evaluate the development of today's riding?
"Today's riding is a little shocking, considering the lack of knowledge and ability and the harshness and forcefulness of the training methods. In the past riders took more time in the careful and correct training of the horse. They also took into account the abilities, the age, and the current state of the horse. Horses are so much better nowadays. Picture-perfect horses are being bred with unbelievable natural movement. To the contrary, riding has significantly worsened because the good trainers are gone. Classical dressage training teaches that the horse is gymnasticized so that the walk is preserved, the trot is made more beautiful through increasing collection, and the extended trot is developed. There is a clear moment of suspension, meaning the horse 'flies' to where his front foot is pointing and doesn't pull it back because he is 'thrashing about' out of pure tension. You can say that dressage riding has not progressed. Dressage sport has split into two schools: one that exercises 'hyperflexion' and achieves questionable results, and the other that tries to follow the path of correct training, which is actually good for the horse. Unfortunately, the latter is not recognized as well by judges because they too lack fundamental knowledge. This is the tricky part: as long as performances that force the horse's obedience in extreme and unusual ways are rewarded with medals, then little will change."

How important are psychological aspects like trust and a relationship between horse and rider in dressage?
"The psychology of the horse is generally far undervalued in training. The horse also feels joy, motivation, pain, and sadness, and seeks positive contact with the rider. Horses learn much more easily and quickly when the encounter with the human is positive and patient, when the horse is encouraged to participate in the work, and when his participation is appropriately rewarded. Since every horse has or develops his own personality and has his own specific issues (just as we humans are all totally different), it is absolutely necessary for the rider to deal with the individual character and capabilities of her

Georg Wahl

Georg Wahl was a Bereiter under Alois Podhajsky and became the head Bereiter at the Spanish Riding School in Vienna. He was known for being Christine Stückelberger's trainer—she dominated the dressage scene for years on Granat, a wonderful mover who was considered quite difficult.

horse. She should observe carefully and note: To what does the horse react positively or negatively? What are the weaknesses that need to be supported? What are the strengths that the rider wants to maintain? It is the small things that make a good rider.

Christine Stückelberger with her mare Ravenna.

The So-Called "School of Modern Riding"

Do All Roads Really Lead to Rome?

The Dutch dressage riders dominated the European Championship in 2009 and cleaned up the gold medals. They used a manner of riding which they call the "new Dutch school." Many of their techniques would also be recognized as "LDR" (low, deep, and round), Rollkur, and hyperflexion. Since these methods, which aren't limited to Dutch riders, are continually criticized, those who choose to promote them try to not only justify their techniques, but also to represent them as other, more modern ways of training the sport horse.

Those who believe in these methods describe their "school" as a "new revolutionary riding method" with the extraordinary claim of bringing psychology, natural horsemanship, and science together.

Proponents of this new school of thought suggest that their methods represent a further evolution of the classical, horse-friendly riding culture. In actuality, their techniques stray far from the intentions and results of the classical teachings that are still the true basis for today's national and international dressage sport. I will explain

Here is a typical picture of "modern" training methods at work in a test. The horse's back is dropped; there is absolute elevation (see p. 156); no flexing of the haunches is evident; and the horse's tail is swishing in agitation.

this further with the help of classical sources and modern scientific knowledge over the next several pages.

When you study these "modern" methods from the standpoint of the horse, it is not another, shorter, or more efficient road to Rome, but rather a path with a very different destination.

I am reminded of the famous drawing of "horse heaven" and William Cavendish, the Duke of Newcastle. He was a baroque English horse trainer who to my mind was very taken with himself. He is credited with having invented the draw reins, and he dominated all his horses in a manner we would possibly now, after reading this book, refer to as "predatory." In one of his books he had himself drawn in "horse heaven" with all the horses he had trained honoring him. The saying, "He who dominates, is beloved," comes to mind here. Even 300 years ago we tried to justify the exploitation of horses for the satisfaction of personal vanity.

The school of thought that propagates LDR and hyperflexion doesn't just use an unnatural, overflexed posture, it relies on the total domination of the horse.

The Arguments of the New School of Riding

This detail of a wall tapestry depicts the classical riding master de la Guérinière.

Is it a "modern evolution"?

The argument that new training methods are an evolutionary combination of psychology, natural horsemanship, and science all together for the first time can be refuted using classical sources.

"Natural horsemanship"—a term that has become quite popular since the 1980s in conjunction with the popular horse training techniques that use communication with horses derived from observation and rejection of abusive methods—was in reality already described over 500 years ago in the original directives of the Spanish Riding School and about 400 BC by Xenophon as a part of the totality of classical teachings. The "nature of the horse" is the foundation of the whole Training Scale.

Natural Horsemanship

This popular term means that training techniques used hinge on communication based on observation of the horse in a natural setting, and they reject abusive or stressful training methods. Value is placed on a harmonious partnership between horse and rider, in that both the horse's body language and his well-being are taken into account.

Many classical masters have successfully explained the psychology of horse and rider in a way that is still supported by scientific knowledge. François Robichon de la Guérinière knew much about what we scientifically understand today as the mind-body continuum, about the learning process of riders and horses, and he understood how to incorporate this knowledge in his method.

Has equestrian sport improved?

The supporters of the modern training methods claim that equestrian sport has changed for the better in the last decade and credit this change to the rise of new training techniques. Supposedly, Rollkur and hyperflexion have led "to a new dimension in equestrian sport" with impressive achievements and continually improving performances.

They maintain that these methods, when correctly used, yield relaxed and obedient horses. As proof they offer that for more than 10 years all of the most important titles at the top of dressage sport have

---

François Robichon de la Guérinière

François Robichon de la Guérinière was, in 1733, the first to describe a systematic training system for the horse that didn't use force. He is considered the founder of classical riding art. He developed the classical independent seat, which is still considered the ideal today.

been won by riders who have worked in this way. These riders credit their success to the round and deep training method refined in the Netherlands.

Using LDR, Rollkur, and hyperflexion, horses are supposedly positively developed: they are more supple with lighter connection, move with more strength and feel better to the rider.

They maintain that horses trained in this way are easier to straighten (collection isn't really discussed) and the rider has an easier time keeping her horse loose and relaxed. Moreover, this method claims to yield horses that are supposedly more beautiful and better muscled.

These illustrations compare classical training postures (left) with modern training postures (right). As we have discussed, modern training postures don't lead to movement patterns that correspond to the criteria of the Training Scale.

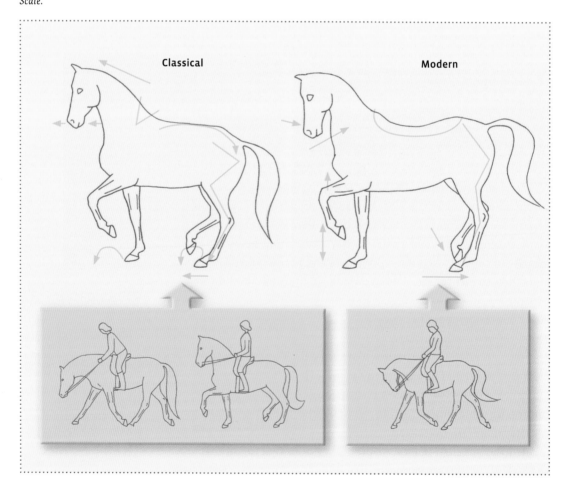

Reality looks different

In my daily work I am frequently confronted with products of these training methods: horses that are tense, have lost trust in humans, are stiff, buck, rear, and frequently "go crazy" when the reins are taken up. I deal with horses that feel they either must protect themselves or have resigned themselves to their fate. Many have become so dangerous that they don't let the rider get on and even attack their trainer on the longe line.

Interestingly, many such cases have been helped by psychological and physical rehabilitation according to the classical method. At the same time their rider is retrained in her seat, and her attitude toward her horse and toward riding itself. My goal is to help the horse forget the "new dimension" that the modern training methods supposedly opened to them so they can begin to enjoy moving again, as well as develop confidence in their own body and in their rider. Their muscling and physical expression change, and I've even seen stereotypical behaviors, such as cribbing, disappear.

1–3 This eight-year-old horse was subjected to modern training methods from his third to his seventh year. He was so psychologically and physically damaged that he developed ulcers that prevented his being ridden.

1

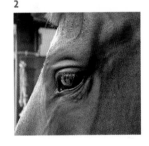

Playing the gender and strength card

The point has been made that today slight women are riding who can't rely on strength. Videos of such "tender maidens" show, however, that the techniques used to make up for what female riders may lack in strength result in the intentional use of major, often painful forces on the horse. For example, holding the reins extra wide (as may be recommended) significantly increases the pressure on the bars of the horse's mouth.

2

In his book *Tug of War*, Dr. Gerd Heuschmann explains how the "lever arm" ratios in the head and poll of the horse (the length of the lever that the rider has available for his rein influence) potentiates the power of the rider. According to Heuschmann's calculations, lever ratios of about 1:10 with a weight of 66 pounds of force (lbf) per hand (on each rein) and a snaffle bit result in about 1,323 lbf being exerted on the horse's poll (see *Tug of War*, p. 102, for a complete explanation of this phenomenon). The curb bit increases this effect many fold. When the rider also leans back and presses her hands downward, pulls them up, or to the side, it is easy to understand how the horse can't free himself from the posture, even if only 120 pounds is sitting on his back.

3

Since the curb bit is unjointed, it is not meant for one-sided, asymmetrical rein aids. The leverage acts harshly on the bars of the horse's mouth.

The strength and weight of the rider is potentiated many times over by the lever effect of the curb bit. The horse's pain continues even when the pull on the reins is relaxed a little since the curb doesn't release immediately.

Do horses "enjoy" hyperflexion?

The proponents of the new modern ways of training dressage horses have a whole host of arguments about why this type of riding is wonderful for the horse. All of these arguments can be refuted when biomechanical and mind-body principles are taken into account. One argument made is that the horse, as a prey animal, connects the low, deep, and round position with security and relaxation (such as that experienced when grazing, drinking, resting).

But, consider, by contrast, the forward-and-downward stretching position with the horse's nose in front of the vertical, which really does have a positive effect on the horse. In this posture the horse, with his eyes placed on the sides of the head, can still see around himself, which is very important to a prey animal. As mentioned, once the horse's nose is behind the vertical, he no longer can see around him; he can no longer see where he is going. In such a situation, a prey animal doesn't feel secure or relaxed. Further, when the horse's natural tendency to balance using his neck is taken from him because his neck is shortened or "rolled" or "curled," and then forcefully held in

Even slight women of moderate strength can put a surprising amount of pressure on the horse's poll and jaw when using their full body in combination with the lever effect of the curb.

place, any sense of general well-being is undermined. He finds it hard to breathe and feels pressure on the poll and on the bars of the jaw.

Those who argue that a deep neck posture is a sign of relaxation in the horse refer to studies from the zoologist E. Slijper, who created the commonly heard "archer's bow and string concept" (1947) and from the Utrecht University in the Netherlands (van Weeren, 2004), where it is explained that a lowering of the head lifts the spine and makes the back arch. But the necessary "fanning" of the vertebrae and relaxation of the long back muscle only happen in the forward-and-downward stretching position. When the horse's neck is so shortened that his nose comes behind the vertical, the opposite effect can be seen in his back. Professor Michael Weishaupt of the University of Zürich discovered in a parallel study that when the horse stiffens his back, his

1–3 When trained in self-defense, prison guards are taught a combination of holds for restraining an inmate that is similar to the hyperflexion method commonly used with dressage horses. By taking away the prisoner's balancing rod (his arms) and then holding his neck, the guards make it impossible for the prisoner to fight back. They can keep the "aggressor" quiet and make him obey their orders.

hindquarters trail out behind him, and the space between the vertebrae where the spinal nerves "exit" the spinal column in the lumbar region are narrowed.

In the often criticized van Weeren study, certain perceived "advantages" of the Rollkur position (for example, for the development of individual muscle groups) are given without critically elucidating the effects on the biomechanics of the whole horse that have been shown in other studies, namely the reduction in ground cover; the inability to step under the body with the hind legs; and the stiffening of the back and lumbar areas.

Proponents also say that the horse demonstrates concentration and focus on his rider when ridden in a deep neck position. Here, cause and effect are confused. Since the rider takes the ability to see from the horse when she rides him deep behind the vertical, she in effect becomes a "seeing-eye dog" for her horse. The horse is dependent on her—not focused on her leadership as a partner.

Finally, it is claimed that a horse ridden with a low, deep, and round neck are more comfortable for the rider. The horse supposedly relaxes his back to such an extent it is easier to sit. He yields to the rider, both physically and mentally, because he feels better working in the deeper neck position.

This is a fallacy founded on a desire for more control. It is incomparably better to sit on a horse that stretches to the bit with his nose in front of the vertical. This horse can see well in front of and round him, and is freely engaged with his rider. The fact that the back, in fact, does not relax in the Rollkur position, is quite visible to the naked eye.

A study from the University of Guelph in Canada by Uta von Borstel (2007) counters the claim that horses "enjoy" modern training methods. Fifteen horses were ridden 30 times through a Y-maze, randomly alternating between sides. Riding through one arm of the Y-maze was always followed by a 20-meter circle ridden in a Rollkur position, whereas riding through the other arm was followed by a 20-meter circle with "normal" poll flexion. Immediately after the conditioning phase of the study, the horses were again repeatedly ridden into the maze; however, riders left it to the horse to decide which arm of the maze to enter. Fourteen of the fifteen horses in the study chose the side that led to "normal" poll flexion.

Being ridden in a posture similar to that a policeman uses when taking a criminal into custody is humiliating to the horse.

Horses ridden using modern training methods often appear similar to a sagging suspension bridge—their back doesn't arch upward but rather drops downward, with tight back muscles, trailing hind legs, and a blocked lumbar area.

Does muscle development come from passive stretching?

Another reason people claim using postures that are different from those we know from classical riding is of benefit is that the musculature of the horse can supposedly be improved more efficiently. Unfortunately, the recommendation of so-called "strength training" of muscles through passive stretching doesn't agree with today's sport science and training practices. Even in human athletics it is not customary to execute localized stretching exercises while at the same time stressing other body regions. Horses that are routinely worked according to modern methods demonstrate how this doesn't work by their appearance: Their upper neck musculature is not clearly pronounced, although they have a visibly developed muscling on the underside of their neck. They lack croup musculature. On the whole, horses that work at the upper levels via these techniques are "square" or "thick" in appearance, but they are not well-muscled.

Is science on the side of hyperflexion?

As must be apparent by now, the fact that this manner of riding is really about human dominance is hidden behind a facade of explanations. Some trainers will stop at nothing in their attempts to justify their actions, "re-interpreting" the results of scientific studies for their own advantage.

For example, as evidence that modern training methods improve

In hyperflexion, muscle groups other than those required according to the Training Scale are conditioned and trained. Instead of the musculature of the upper neck, an undesirable muscling on the underside of the neck is developed. The back is tight, and instead of the hindquarters, the forehand musculature develops.

elasticity of the horse's movements and reduce the stress of dressage training, they have referenced the already mentioned study by Professor Michael Weishaupt (see p. 189), the head of the Sports Medicine Performance Center at the University of Zürich Equine Clinic, which was built in cooperation with the universities in Uppsala, Sweden, and Utrecht, The Netherlands. In fact, Dr. Weishaupt sees no advantages for the quality of the movement and instead clear dangers and disadvantages in terms of the horse's health.

The study compared the movements of horses without riders on a treadmill with the neck in one of six different, defined positions (see illustrations to the right):

1 A "free" or natural neck position.
2 Nose just in front of the vertical.
3 Nose just behind the vertical.
4 "Rollkur" (extreme overflexion).
5 Neck raised high.
6 Long reins, with the nose distinctly in front of the vertical (a young horse posture, long and low).

As might be expected, Posture 5 had the most distinct effect on back activity and the length of the horse's steps, since the horse's neck was aggressively elevated and the back was pressed down. With "Rollkur," the steps were shortened and there was also a more defined up-and-down movement of the back.

In an interview with the German equestrian magazine Cavallo (August 2007), Dr. Weishaupt explained what he had learned about the effect the Rollkur position (without a rider) has on movement. He said he finds it almost "unthinkable" that even a moment would be spent at the walk or quiet trot in this position, and he sees absolutely no advantage for the horse's movement apparatus. At the most, Rollkur produces an increased "movement awareness" in the horse—but only when done for a few seconds and the horse can relax afterward and reposition himself. When a horse is worked for a longer period of time with a "rolled" or "curled" up neck, often with the head positioned to the side, stressors are created and there is an increased risk of injury.

The position brings absolutely nothing to the table in terms of

A Potemkin Village

The term "Potemkin Village" is a saying that refers to a "fake village" that is built only to impress—in other words, a beautiful facade constructed to hide an actual sad reality. It is said by some that Russian minister Grigory Potemkin erected fake settlements along the banks of the Dnieper River in order to fool Empress Catherine II during her visit to Crimea in 1787, hiding the true condition of the land.

1
2
3
4
5
6

When using Rollkur, the step sequence and purity of the walk rhythm suffer from the stiffening in the horse's back and lumbar regions.

improved hind end activity since the horse's hind legs don't step under his body. Dr. Weishaupt added: "It is much easier to manipulate the reins instead of working on the hind end with the seat."

Dr. Weishaupt evaluates the phrase "positive range of motion" in conjunction with the movement of the horse's back differently than proponents of modern training methods. In the Rollkur posture, the back lifts more intensely so that the middle portion, where the saddle sits, is overloaded. It isn't supported in the same way it is when the horse is ridden in a forward-and-downward stretch. In the deep, round posture the openings between the vertebrae, which nerves pass through, are narrowed, and the transition between the lumbar vertebrae and the sacrum is overstretched, achieving the opposite effect of encouraging hind leg activity in collection. This is why horses ridden in Rollkur trail their hind end out behind and can't step under their body. Their balance changes massively, and they use other muscles and leverage to compensate.

Range of motion

Range of motion refers to the distance and direction a joint can move between the flexed position and the extended position, without injury.

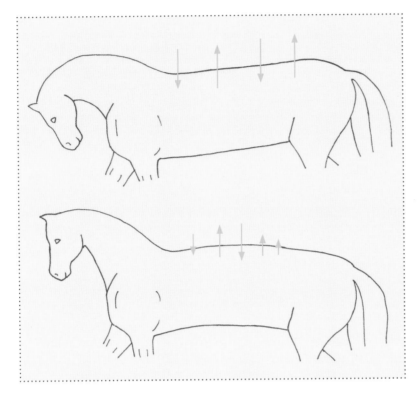

Back movement is much more intense in the Rollkur position, but the horse holds the back and moves it up and down stiffly, in contrast to the soft arch and wavelike motions in the back of a classically trained horse.

Dr. Gerd Heuschmann, veterinarian, Bereiter, and author of the international bestselling book *Tug of War: Classical versus "Modern" Dressage*, is completely aligned with Dr. Weishaupt on this matter. When considering measurements from studies of horses on the treadmill, he found the so-called "positive range of motion" to be anything but positive. The horse's back does lift and sink with somewhat greater amplitude since the back muscle is stiff in a hyperflexed position. However, there is a lack of the desired wavelike, swinging movement. The back lifts and sinks like a stiff board. This actually makes it hard for a rider to sit the horse well.

The pain that is a consequence of a rigid back combined with the overstretching of the lumbar area is extremely uncomfortable for the horse. The horse's gaits lose their purity. The rhythm of the walk is lost, and there is a broken diagonal footfall at the trot. The hind leg doesn't come forward with the activity of the corresponding front leg since it is trailing out behind. Instead of round, elastic movements

The Xenophon Society

Xenophon, the "Society for the Preservation of the Classical Equestrian Culture," is named after a Greek scholar who lived about 400 BC. His work *On Horsemanship* is regarded as perhaps the first treatise on humane horse training methods. Representatives of the Xenophon Society strive to educate the horse community about the consequences of many of the current training methods used to prepare young horses for competition (www.xenophon-klassisch.org).

where each hoof is set down out of a swinging motion, the horse is forced to stamp his feet, and in trot extensions, throw his front legs out. We can't even pretend to talk about more elasticity here. This change in the mechanics of the horse's movement cannot be considered positive from a veterinary perspective, since it is clearly damaging to the joints and the support apparatus.

Another study done by sports physiologist Eric van Breda (2006) has been claimed to prove Grand Prix horses trained in a hyperflexed position are not stressed. The study analyzed heart rate variability in seven pleasure horses as compared to five Grand Prix horses being trained in hyperflexion. Heart rate variability was analyzed half an hour after the horses were fed and after training for fifteen minutes. While the study concluded that it did not find that dressage horses ridden using the Rollkur method suffered more stress than the pleasure horses, van Breda himself admitted the study's results should be carefully considered. "Our results," van Breda and his cowriters observed, "must be interpreted with care because no behavioral measurements have been taken into account... Although these preliminary data provide no evidence for a detrimental effect of the Rollkur training method on stress and/or pain in these horses, the number of horses in this study warrants more research. Finally, it has to be taken into account that heart rate variability has, to the best of our knowledge, not yet been proven as an established measure for chronic pain."

Does it all come down to rider "feel"?

Every training method stands or falls with its correct or incorrect application. Proponents of modern training methods say that the use of Rollkur is influenced by the amount of "feel" that a rider either has or doesn't.

Some maintain that when modern training methods do not work, it is due to poor rider feel and is not the fault of the techniques being used.

I disagree with this based on my own studies in which I have examined how to measure the body-mind capabilities of riders. In connection with the Van Hall Larenstein Institute in Leeuwarden, The Netherlands, I am currently overseeing two dissertations focused on these aspects of rider ability and their influence on the well-being and biomechanics of the horse. Even though these studies are not yet complete, some results are already of interest. In a study at the lower levels of dressage, all the horses worked according to modern methods showed significantly more signs of discomfort and tension than the horses worked according to classical training methods. This was true even when the riders using classical training methods made

Along with the broken diagonal footfall at the trot, there is a difference between the classical and modern movement patterns at piaffe and passage, as shown in these illustrations.

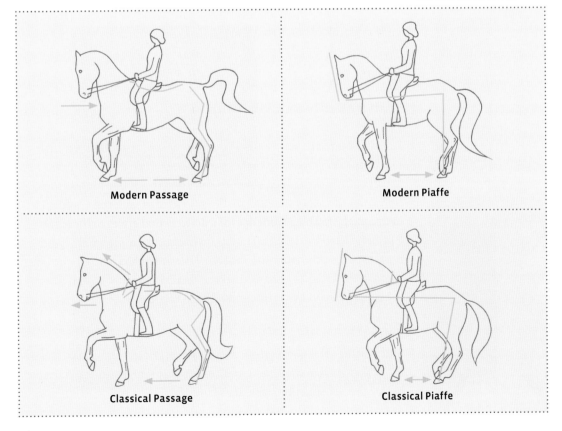

Modern Passage

Modern Piaffe

Classical Passage

Classical Piaffe

Many poorly trained riders at the lower levels disturb their horse more than they support him in his efforts to perform. They turn to modern training methods because they think they are easier.

mistakes due to insufficient ability or perhaps lack of feel.

From my experience as a riding instructor and judge, and based on studies I have conducted, I don't share the optimism that better horses and improved riding quality have led to an improvement in equestrian sports over the past decade. As indicated in the study I cited on p. 85 that tested a representative sample of 30 dressage riders at the lower levels, it is clear that most riders today make their horse's job more difficult because they are poorly trained in the following areas: seat, posture, communication, and giving the aids. Since almost all the riders in the study were riding young horses that they were training themselves rather than experienced school horses, we can easily imagine the detrimental effects of their riding on their mounts.

Since so many new or beginner dressage riders want to copy the hyperflexion method that promises success and quickly, we are faced with a combination of insufficient ability and techniques that are harsh and not in the horse's best interest. This is an ugly situation that an international educational effort is trying to end.

The Methods in Comparison

This horse, ridden according to modern methods, is clearly uncomfortable.

Let's look at the principles and consequences of the modern training methods as compared to those of the classical school of thought, specifically in regards to biomechanics and mind-body aspects of the horse. On the pages that follow, I've provided the ten training "rules" I've seen offered by proponents of the "New Dutch School" and the Academy Bartels (the educational institute run by Joep and Tineke Bartels of The Netherlands), and then I've described how we often see them interpreted by today's riders, as well as compared them to what is expected when we train a horse classically.

Rule #1

Give a young horse the chance to get used to you and to develop trust in you. When the horse has confidence, he will relax in various positions. When the horse can relax, he will lower his head.

How is this interpreted? This relaxation is achieved through riding forward at a too fast tempo. The rider's hands are held wide apart and very low.

What do we see in practice? The horse is "held" in front (with wide hands and low, "buried" fists) and isn't encouraged to bring the hindquarters under his body by stretching to the bit. The horse is usually ridden in an exaggerated tempo on the forehand. This is different from riding the horse forward-and-downward, since the horse reaches downward behind the vertical and against the rider's hands.

Forward-and-downward work is the way to encourage a horse to relax and become supple, according to classical training.

Consequences: A great deal of pressure is put on the bars of the horse's mouth and on the poll when the hands are held wide and low in this way. Consequently, it isn't true that the horse let's his head drop due to relaxation. He bends under force, with his neck flexing incorrectly between the second and fourth neck vertebrae.

Classical perspective: The classical school abides by the same rule, but the difference is that trust is built by the human as she consciously supports the horse in his effort to find a new balance and develop a new body awareness. This happens at a calm, regular tempo and in a forward-and-downward stretching posture. The horse should relax his back and stretch to the bit. It isn't about the head "dropping," but rather about stretching the neck and head to the front and down. This is achieved through activation of the hindquarters, not by fixing the hands in a wide-and-low position.

This horse's head is forcefully pulled to his chest. He can't relax in either body or mind.

Rule #2
Train for tempo control: refine the reaction to the leg and rein aids.

How is this interpreted? The leg aid is understood by most as "pounding" or "thumping." The horse learns that he may suddenly be bombarded at any time with the rider "stepping on the gas" (leg) or "putting on the brakes" (reins). He reacts with panic, especially to the leg because he is expected to be "quick to the leg."

According to the classical perspective, the horse must always be able to stretch forward-and-downward. If he is unable to do so, then something has gone wrong in his training.

Holding the reins wide and pressing the hands downward, as is taught by modern methods, doesn't lead to forward-and-downward stretching, but instead forces the horse's head down and in.

What do we see in practice? The horse is driven forward without preparation for the change in gait, pace, or tempo and at the same time stopped by the hands. Half-halts aren't used. The position of the horse's neck is not adjusted as it should be according to pace and tempo (frame lengthening).

Consequences: Since the horse is ridden with the nose behind the vertical, he can't step under his body with his hindquarters and reacts with tight hocks and by shooting forward in movements that aren't round. Since he can't lengthen his frame as necessary according to change in speed and pace, he has to stiffen his back. When the back can't swing, it can't help "soften" his leg movements.

Classical perspective: The horse isn't "accelerated," "stopped," or "steered" in isolation. The horse is prepared for changes in movement, pace, and tempo with half-halts from the rider's seat so that he learns to adjust in response to impulses from the rider and to match his movement pattern to changing expectations he senses through the rider's seat. His frame is allowed to lengthen when his stride is lengthened. In schooling sessions, he is prepared with transitions and pace changes for work involving increased engagement and collection.

Rule #3
Don't give rein and leg aids at the same time. The horse cannot understand it.

How is this interpreted? Rein aids are differentiated only in terms of "stopping" and "yielding," and there is no mention of diagonal aids, straightness, bending, the inside leg, or the guarding leg.

What do we see in practice? The horse is constantly held by the rider's hands. There is permanent pressure on the horse's bars and poll, even when the legs or spurs are used. The seat is used to lean back while the hands are still active. The horse moves crookedly and stiff in turns.

Consequences: The horse gets used to permanent pressure on his bars and poll—then, all of a sudden he is kicked. Since he can't

When the rider asks the horse to stop without using her legs, but instead only with her hands as she leans back, the horse's hindquarters do not come under his body as is desirable.

anticipate this "aid," he reacts reflexively. Unfortunately, round, consciously planned movements are impossible.

Classical perspective: Seat, leg, and hand give combinations of subtle movement impulses in predetermined sequences. Individual aids aren't used in isolation. A constant interplay of movement impulses are exchanged between rider and horse in the form of a dialogue.

Rule #4
Teach the horse to "give" to a resisting hand.

How is this interpreted? The horse should learn to stop and yield as a reaction to two different rein aids. "Chewing" and yielding is achieved via the reins, not through the seat and moving together and the horse's hindquarters coming further under his body. Riders learn to work from front to back, instead of vice versa.

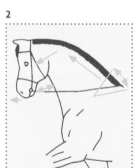

1 *In modern training methods, submission is desired at any price.*

2 *This illustration depicts how, in contrast, the vertebrae of the withers should "fan" as the horse stretches his neck and head to the bit, seeking the contact, according to classical theory.*

What do we see in practice? Through powerful forces applied on the poll and bars of the jaw, the horse's nose is pulled behind the vertical. Bending at the poll is confused with suppleness and relaxation on the part of the horse. Likewise, grinding teeth is confused with relaxed chewing.

Classical perspective: The horse doesn't have to yield to the hand; rather he is motivated by the rider to stretch to the bit. The rider doesn't accomplish this with the hands, but primarily through her seat. She brings the horse under from behind. Her independent hands are in harmony with the horse's mouth as they interact with a conversational connection.

Rule #5
Develop a game of Question and Answer through tempo changes.

How is this interpreted? The horse is continually unbalanced by contradictory aids and being "flexed" in all directions as changes of tempo are ridden.

What do we see in practice? The horse is held in a fixed neck position with pressure on the poll and bars while he is alternately kicked forward and pulled to a stop, or overflexed to the side while ridden at a too-fast tempo.

Consequences: The horse learns that he must always react immediately even when the aids are contradictory and he is unbalanced or his movement is blocked. The game of "Question and Answer" could be rephrased as "give an order and expect an immediate reaction." The horse is not allowed to ask his own questions or comment on the game.

Classical perspective: We should strive for a dialogue with our horse through the primary aids (see p. 59) and by accepting information that the horse is allowed to contribute. The horse perceives the dialogue of motion as a dance—he is led by his partner but still decides himself what he will do next. From this communication arise

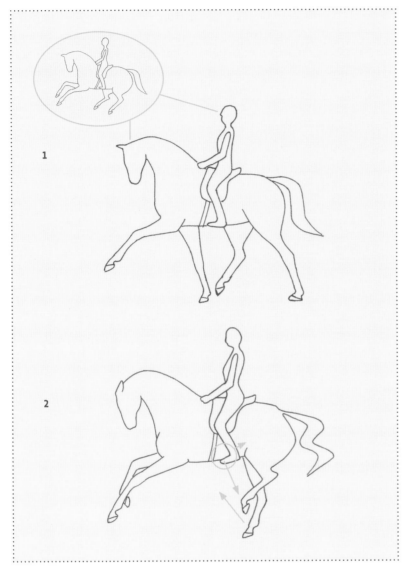

1 *Classical: Engaging in a harmonious dialogue of motion and creating a movement plan together.*

2 *Modern: Playing the "Question and Answer Game," without a two-way dialogue or a movement plan.*

fluid, planned movements executed without unnecessary excitement or panic-type reactions.

Rule #6
When the horse can be sent forward or slowed at any moment, then work on posture control can begin: invite your horse's head to "fall."

1

2

1 *Many positions used in modern dressage training are not functional from a biomechanical viewpoint.*

2 *The horse's forehand is usually heavily loaded (it assumes more weight than the hindquarters—even more weight than usual) in such positions.*

How is this interpreted? The "philosophy" here is that when the horse has learned to give to the hand, he can be ridden "down" through the poll. "The hand becomes a flexible side rein," says Bartels. It is another "game" where there is variation in different positions involving more or less "rolling" of the horse's neck.

What do we see in practice? The horse gets more and more controllable through his neck position and simultaneous pressure exerted on his neck and the bars of his jaw. He must move in postures that do not make physiological or biomechanical sense.

Classical perspective: The emphasis is not on the rider changing the horse's neck position but on varying the amount of engagement and collection in the hindquarters. The horse adjusts his own neck carriage according to the level of collection, and the rider allows him this option. Any attempt to manually position the nose line and the poll disturbs the work of the hindquarters and the swing of the horse's back muscles. "Relative elevation" (see p. 74) is achieved through the flexion of the haunches that is needed for collection.

Rule #7
Work on the athletic development of the horse through shortening and lengthening.

How is this interpreted? The horse is simply ridden behind the bit and moves with hesitant steps forwards.

What do we see in practice? The horse is never truly lengthened with his nose in front of the vertical. He cannot stretch to the bit with confidence since he is used to having to "give" to the hand. We often see the reins hanging with a loop, which is interpreted by some as a sign of the horse voluntarily staying in the Rollkur position.

Consequences: "Spectacular" movement featuring the horse's legs being pulled up high or thrown out in an exaggerated fashion are the result of the haunches not being sufficiently flexed. During training the horse is on the forehand and forced to throw his legs out instead of gathering his weight over his hind end in collection. His movements are panicked, stamping, and no longer round. The trot is broken in the diagonal since the back muscle isn't working in a relaxed state and the hind legs are trailing. The walk is no longer pure since the horse's movement is prevented from swinging over the back through to his nose.

Classical perspective: Spectacular movements aren't the goal of dressage, rather the development of natural, calm but powerful movements, including a pure walk that swings over the back and a trot where the front legs are flung out more quickly or higher than their corresponding hind legs (in the diagonal pair).

Gait, pace, and tempo changes without allowing the horse to adjust his frame can lead to cramping.

Rule #8
Work on removing all blockages.

How is this interpreted? Modern training methods would have us not only be riders but physical therapists, fitness trainers, and psychologists for the horse, as well. We should do our best to "massage" and ride physical and mental blockages away by playing with and varying tempo and neck position.

What do we see in practice? The horse is blocked in the lumbar area from the "rolling" of his neck, as well as his stiff back and painful

Here we can see the kind of "spectacular" movements with the legs being thrown out from a locked back that we've come to expect in the modern-day dressage arena. This kind of movement causes blockages in the horse that are not easily removed.

"Rolling" or "curling" the horse's neck causes absolute elevation (see p. 156). This is not collection.

poll. It seems like it must be a joke to claim that the horse's back can be "massaged" by a rider weighing about 130 pounds during strenuous work with the neck overflexed and bent in both directions.

Classical perspective: Basic training according to the Scale should ensure that the horse doesn't stiffen or develop blockages in his body. The criteria of rhythm, suppleness, and straightness must always be kept in mind.

Rule #9
By working on tempo and position control, collection develops automatically.

How is this interpreted? Collection is replaced by absolute elevation (the hindquarters fail to step under the horse's body).

What do we see in practice? The horse's hindquarters are not under him in transitions. He may consistently step back at the halt but is never corrected.

Consequences: Riding dressage exercises that encourage collection, such as transitions and lateral movements, or performing piaffe at too high a speed with a deep neck and the nose behind the vertical, prevents the haunches from flexing properly. The exercises can't achieve their goal. The horse's area of support isn't reduced and his hind legs don't begin to carry more weight. The horse moves with a stiff or dropped back.

Classical perspective: Every pace and tempo has an appropriate frame. It is not logical to ride at a high speed with a shortened frame. Engagement and later collection develop through targeted work of the hind end, maintaining a loose, swinging back and an appropriate neck position. It is a slow training process through which the horse continually gets closer to the goal in a biomechanical sense while he develops coordination and power.

Rule #10
The horse should be physically and mentally "open" to the rider.

How is this interpreted? If we have followed all the rules of modern dressage training, then we have achieved qualitatively better training and don't need the Training Scale, or its concept of throughness anymore.

What do we see in practice? A stiff horse with a dropped back and a stiff, "fixed" poll, a broken diagonal at the trot, and a walk that is no longer pure. His movements are no longer round, but stamping. On curves this horse doesn't bend and he doesn't collect by flexing his haunches properly. This method confuses instantaneous "panic" reactions at the push of a button to be the same as "being open to the rider."

This horse is shut off from the outside world. He can't be open mentally because the stress is too great.

Classical perspective: The classical teachings strive for the horse to be open to the rider through all steps of training done according to the criteria of the Training Scale. In a dialogue of motion, the horse works actively with the rider and is therefore motivated of his own accord. In the ideal for which we strive, there is complete harmony between the two. Horse and rider want the same thing and work together to achieve it.

Today's Controversy in Equestrian Sports

It Is About the Horse's Well-being

There is intense controversy today, both within the world of equestrian sports, and in general discussion surrounding it. The excesses associated with equestrian sports are in the crossfire of criticism. Even classical theory is under debate. Ultimately, the question we all need to ask is whether the well-being of the horse is being considered as he is used in sports, for pleasure, as a therapy animal, or for other purposes.

The argument between different philosophies as to how to best interact with the horse periodically flames up anew, and has since the times of Xenophon, de la Guérinière, Baucher, Grisone, Fillis, and Podhajsky (to name only a few). Today's controversy happens to be especially important because equestrian sports have never been more popular. In addition, it is now also "big business." As it is so often when money, power, and competition play a role, ethics and human assumption of responsibility are left by the wayside. Horses are degraded to production-line outputs and are little more than a means to an end. While their riders enjoy great popularity and have at their disposal a public relations machine, the horses have no way to lobby for their own cause. Many horses disappear "out the back door," their body ruined early in their career. Others survive inappropriate treatment and forceful training techniques only to suffer psychologically and lose their integrity as a horse.

The elite riders and trainers of the international equestrian scene should be setting a good example. Theoretically, this shouldn't even be in question because the Fédération Equestre Internationale (FEI) established in its rules that the well-being of the horse should come before all else. Additionally, it defined guidelines for training and testing that should make all discussion as to what is correct training and what is not irrelevant. Riders and trainers who don't follow these guidelines in training and showing should be eliminated from the top competitions.

Despite all this, in the last few years it has seemed as if there is a general acceptance of behavior that is harsh and forceful toward horses at the highest levels of international competition. It is unfathomable that training methods are made to seem harmless when the horse's pain and tension is visible to the naked eye.

Horses have distinct, individual personalities. They should be respected by those who ride and train them at all levels and in all kinds of equestrian sports.

A Study: How the Horse Exits Following a Test

Because of changes in the world of dressage, top competition is now about a lot more than just achieving harmony with the horse. Consequently, horses are trained and shown in such a way that we can see in their body expression that there is, in fact, a complete lack of harmony and that the horse doesn't feel comfortable performing the exercises asked of him.

How a horse leaves the arena after a test is to me, very meaningful. As part of a study, I have watched how 30 rider-and-horse combinations exited the arena following a test, and then had the same group evaluated by equine bodyworkers, judges, and even non-riders (after educating them on how to assess horse expressions).

The evaluators were asked to exclusively assess the behavior criteria that reflect a horse's well-being. Interestingly, all of those who participated in the study, whether riders or non-riders with more or less technical knowledge, used these criteria to give identical evaluations. I therefore feel the results of this study are very reliable.

The horses that were least able to leave the arena calmly after a test also exhibited behavior patterns that suggest that they were not "internally balanced" (focused and relaxed) during the test, regardless of whether or not the test was correctly ridden. Other horses showed no or only minimal signs of stress even though their rider made mistakes and asked the horse to fix them.

It was especially interesting to examine—systematically and empirically—the technical and interpersonal aspects of the mind-body interaction between rider and horse that most impact the well-being of the horse in his work. I must note that in this study, there weren't enough riders working in hyperflexion available to participate and provide solid results concerning that specific training method.

When we consider the horse's pain and his blue tongue, the pat from his triumphant rider is a Judas kiss.

1

2

1 The horse's facial expressions send a clear message of his state of mental and physical well-being.

2 Wringing the tail is not only a sign of stress, most likely caused by the rider, but also indicates tension in the horse's back.

The study criteria

Physical signs of well-being were defined as:
- Harmonious flow of motion and appropriate rhythm.
- "Roundness" of movement.
- "Quiet" facial expression.
- Relaxed poll and jaw.
- Calm, attentive eye.
- Relaxed ears moving appropriately for the situation, focused on the rider and the surroundings.
- Regular breathing with emphasis on exhaling (snorting).
- Sweaty areas appropriate for the movement, training intensity, and the condition of the horse.
- Peaceful and harmonious physical expression in motion.
- Logical tension and relaxation of relevant muscle groups.
- Positive general body expression.
- Tail swish that matches the swing of the horse's back.

Characteristics of the horse evaluated during the test:
- Breathing, development of sweat.
- Eyes, facial expression.
- Swishing of the tail.
- Movement of the ears.
- Muscle tension.
- General body expression.

Characteristics of the horse evaluated after the test:
- General body expression.
- Interest in the surroundings.
- Trust in the rider.
- Confidence in the situation.
- Regularity in gaits.
- Calm walk.
- Neck position.
- Back activity from the hind legs to the poll.
- Mouth activity.

Characteristics of the horse for comparative evaluation:

- Tension vs. relaxation.
- Contentment vs. insecurity.
- Calm breathing and snorting vs. holding the breath.
- Eyes wandering around with interest vs. being fixed on "nothing."
- Quiet and calm vs. stressed and hyperactive.
- Contentment with his own performance vs. undirected excitement.
- Healthy suppleness vs. tension that looks unhealthy.
- Eagerness vs. hurriedness.
- Enjoys applause and praise vs. overreacts to applause and doesn't react to the praise.
- Ears moving around appropriately and focused on the rider vs. moving nervously.
- Reasonable vs. unreasonable excitement.

The contrast in physical expression between this rider and her horse upon completion of a test couldn't be greater.

A Controversy with a Long History

It is often argued that the excesses that have been seen over time can never be stopped since they happen wherever there are people. That may be true to some extent; however, when the excesses are no longer an infrequent deviation but instead threaten to become the new "norm," then we should think about taking action.

The handwriting is on the wall. At seven or eight years old, the dressage horse isn't even a fully mature adult, nor has he reached his optimal peak performance capability. Yet, more and more horses at this age suffer from physical, psychological, and behavioral issues. The problem doesn't lie only with the dressage industry, of course—the same happens with jumpers, Western sport horses, and in all types of other equestrian settings. I fear it isn't just that too many riders don't know enough about horses; I think the horse awakens different needs within humans. The horse can be used as a tool to fulfill our desire for power and success.

As long as horses and humans have worked together, riders have used harsh, forceful, sometimes cruel training methods. Even in the full bloom of the classical riding culture there were depictions in illustration and sculpture, as well as written accounts, that show how man can create a push-button machine out of a horse by using dominance and a combination of mechanical and psychological "tricks" that ensure "good functioning."

Some historical proponents of questionable techniques in horse training were Grisone, the Duke of Newcastle, Pfitzner, Fillis, and Baucher, all of whom wrote about intentionally making the horse "insecure" through the use of stimulus-response training principles (see p. 168, sidebar).

Similar to what we see today, bits and auxiliary equipment were used to force the horse into uncomfortable positions. Usually the horse was also in some way prevented from using his neck as a balancing rod, his head, neck, and poll "fixed" in place, and with them, his back. He was, like today, forced to reactively adjust to his rider without the rider giving him the chance to exercise his own initiative or plan his own movements.

More than 50 years ago, Alois Podhajsky presented a paper at a

Many of the sport horses we see already damaged by poor training techniques are only seven or eight years old.

meeting of the German Judges Association in Warendorf, where he warned against the danger of the FEI accepting such methods as I've described. His presentation applies word for word to the state of today's equestrian sports. Other proponents of the classical, horse-friendly way of riding that has been the basis of international guidelines for horse sports also raised their voices when at times it became all too clear that such methods threatened to become widespread.

In the 1970s, Russian dressage riders were criticized for riding their horses in absolute elevation, with shortened necks and dropped backs, at the piaffe and passage. The journalist Horst Stern has shown how hyperflexion makes jumpers totally submissive as they are forced to complete challenging courses practically blind.

Professor Heinz Meyer created a furor with an article he wrote for the German horse magazine Reiten St. Georg (November, 1992). In it he maintained that nothing but a desire for total dominance of the horse and a lack of consideration for the undesirable consequences for his movement apparatus and psyche stood behind the deep and round techniques practiced by dressage Olympic champion Nicole Uphoff.

Since these past examples, we have used the term "Rollkur" for methods of "rolling" and overflexing the neck. When the riding style had a name, it seemed to become even more popular, and it has become well known due to its use by two of the most celebrated dressage riders in the world: Anky van Grunsven and Isabell Werth.

Alois Podhajsky

Alois Podhajsky was an officer in the Austrian cavalry and an international dressage and jumping competitor before he became head of the Spanish Riding School in Vienna. He led the Spanish Riding School for many years while continuing to be active as a dressage rider and judge. His book *My Horses, My Teachers,* is an international favorite.

Dressage Today

The Dutch Olympian Anky van Grunsven and her trainer Sjef Janssen advertise in seminars, and in print and online articles, their method that has led to success. They describe it as low, deep, and round (LDR), and attribute the winning of many medals to the horse's back being worked optimally through the "rolling up" of his neck and stretching over the back in a way never before practiced in riding art.

By training with the head in varying positions behind the vertical and with extreme lateral positioning of the neck, they claim the horse is better prepared for his test in the arena where much less is asked of him than in training. The horse finds the test itself easy.

We still see extreme techniques in the warm-up ring, even after the FEI issued new guidelines.

There is of course some sense in saying we should confront the horse in training with a certain level of stress in order to improve his fitness and raise his endurance (see our discussion of optimal training on p. 92, where I discuss the fact that I don't believe stress is ever a good thing in training). But in the long term, their training with stress only creates more stress.

Since riding extremely behind the vertical with the chin against the chest deviates profoundly from the postures described in the FEI guidelines, the terms "training position" and "competition position" have been introduced. The classical position appropriate for competition is supposedly too stiff, meaning the horse shouldn't be ridden that way in training. In this way the "bad example" of successful competitive riders has been condoned.

Legalized by the FEI?

The process of accepting modern dressage training methods as the

The horse may be ridden up to ten minutes in this position for suppling purposes.

new "norm" took about ten years. It peaked when the FEI not only allowed the awarding of medals to the proponents of Rollkur, but also "legalized" it by adjusting the guidelines against massive protest. Stewards and judges who in the meantime had warned against clearly increasing aggressiveness in the use of LDR techniques for suppling now had to fear being publicly reprimanded. They would be portrayed as jealous of rider successes and accused of acting politically. Even journalists who expressed criticism in horse magazines and individuals who aired their opinions in letters to the editor or online had to fear legal consequences.

Since criticism still wasn't silenced and well known equine experts joined in to challenge the acceptance of modern methods, the FEI finally called for the workshop in Lausanne, Switzerland, in 2006 to hear the different viewpoints. This workshop, frankly, was a disappointment. For example, only a portion of the aforementioned treadmill studies from the Universities of Zürich, Uppsala, and Utrecht were presented since a large amount of the data had not yet been evaluated at that time.

The studies were criticized because the tempo of the treadmill was varied with different neck positions (based on the perception that the horse would move more easily). The results from the different postures were unfortunately only compared with a "natural" position and not against one another. It was still unclear how the rider's weight influences movement with the horse's neck in different positions. In addition, other techniques used with the hyperflexion method weren't tested in the study. All of this limited the power of the evidence.

Neither damage from nor value of the method was shown in Lausanne. It became more or less a question of how long a horse could be expected to be ridden in an extremely overflexed neck position. All the other questionable aspects of these techniques, such as intentionally making the horse insecure and seeking above all else to dominate the horse, didn't come under discussion.

The result was a contradictory statement by the FEI. The method in question was officially designated as "hyperflexion." It was conceded that it was not generally to be recommended, but that if used correctly by professionals, it could be tolerated.

1–2 *We can tell in the competitive arena whether a horse has been worked according to classical or modern methods. Here we see position and flexion of the horse's body in the classical passage (1) and in the modern passage (2). Drawing 2 depicts absolute elevation (see p. 156).*

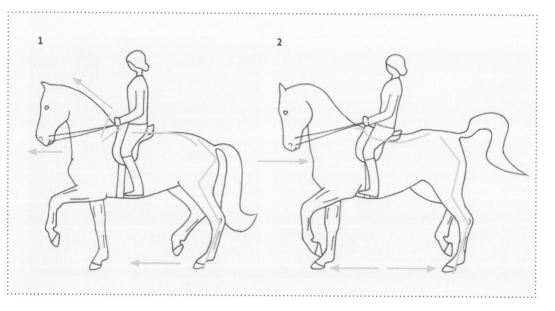

Acceptance through vague criteria

Years have passed since the FEI first took up this matter. The additional studies that the FEI promised to examine haven't been done. Instead, there are new guidelines for stewards. Not only do these new guidelines fail to provide clear criteria for those watching riders and trainers warming up in competitive environments, they now show three accepted training positions, all of which contradict the guidelines of the Training Scale in regard to the seat of the rider and how the horse moves in contact (see illustrations, right).

Long, deep, and round

Animal protection and fair play

There will only be a positive change in the situation when extreme positioning of the head and neck and lateral bending (flexing) for "only" a "short" amount of time are no longer allowed.

Long and low

They go against the well-being of the horse and have no logical training effect other than to achieve dominance. The stewards and technical delegates at our competitions shouldn't have to decide how long they allow predators to sit on top of prey animals in the warm-up area. They should be allowed to stop such riding immediately. That would be in line with putting the welfare of the horse first—after all, the FEI guidelines claim the horse's well-being should be placed above all other considerations. Such a change would also decisively ensure "fair play," as riders would be measured against each other for their actual riding ability and the effectiveness of the partnership with the horse.

Low, deep, and round

None of these three riding positions, all approved by the FEI for use in warm-up, agree with the criteria of the Training Scale—all of the pictures show a horse going behind the vertical.

There are indications that people are trying to get dressage tests changed so that the negative results of modern training methods, which we can see when we watch a horse trained in this manner in a test, are no longer considered when judging. Evaluation points that emphasize the Training Scale criteria (such as collection and purity of the gaits) would disappear from test sheets. It seems only a matter of time until test movements such as halt, walk, and rein-back will also disappear from the tests because they also clearly show whether the horse has fulfilled the principles of classical dressage.

Responsibility of the spectator

The average spectator contributes to the spread of hyperflexion and its offshoots without realizing that she is participating in acts, performed before her very eyes, that range from disrespect for the horse to torment. When more people could empathize with the horse and look more closely, they would surely no longer applaud or cheer when winning comes at the expense of the horse, despite national pride and enthusiasm for the sport.

It is hoped that more riders and horse sport enthusiasts are ready to respect the needs and the essence of the horse and embrace the forms of dialogue humans can have with him. Above all, we should all strive to one day have the chance to "dance" with our horse, or see someone else experiencing such a partnership. Then we will have a

The welfare of the horse should stand above all other considerations.

Horses are loving, social creatures that share with us with their speed and power. They always do their best for us when we treat them as a partner. They deserve someone looking out for their best interests.

clear picture of what a happy horse—or better said, two happy dance partners content with one another—looks like. This image could once again become the ideal expected at the top of the sport of dressage. The horse would then have his own lobby of individuals working for his best interests, rather than their own.

Alois Podhajsky's Paper (1953): More Relevant Today Than Ever

As mentioned in the preceding pages, Alois Podhajsky wrote a paper following the dressage tests at the Olympic Games in London (1948) and Helsinki (1952), which was published in the German magazine St. Georg in 1953 and in the Netherlands in De Hoefslag. It applies word for word today in regards to the current controversies in equestrian sport.

Podhajsky objected most of all to "spectacle" being valued above correct training: "to make the horse quiet, elegant, and obedient through systematic work, so that he becomes pleasing in his motion and comfortable for the rider. The horse should happily subordinate his will to that of the rider. He should unfold in all his beauty and give the rider a pleasant feeling through the careful training and development of his suppleness and agility. All the happiness on earth can be described as found on the back of the horse. But there is no happiness on this earth, neither for the rider nor for the horse, if the rider has to continually fight in any way with his horse, which is unfortunately seen at the highest levels during suppling. But the indifferent and often even unhappy face of the dressage horse that fulfills his duty, sometimes with tired and flat, sometimes with tense and irregular steps, shows that joy on earth is missing."

Podhajsky blamed trainers, instructors, riders, and judges as responsible for the situation. He blamed the trainers and riders because they didn't follow a careful and systematic gymnasticization of the horse in accordance with the criteria of the Training Scale. He blamed them for prefering "spectacular" movement and absolute obedience from the horse over a horse that confidently reached to the bit. He blamed the judges for not showing the riders the way forward with proper evaluation. Acceptance of tension, hesitant steps, and impure gaits in dressage tests legitimizes unsound training methods, resulting in something that has nothing to do with harmony or the joy that can be shared between horse and rider.

Alois Podhajsky

Alois Podhajsky concluded his equestrian career as head of the Spanish Riding School and a dressage judge. In his books he focuses in detail on the mind of the horse.

Open Letter to the FEI

February 3, 2010

Dear Sirs and Madams:

We submit herewith some comments concerning your upcoming roundtable discussion, scheduled for February 9th, at which you will be establishing a final plan for the handling of the topic of Rollkur/hyperflexion.

Those of us who have signed this letter wish to point out sharply that new or amended rules with regard to the accepted classical precepts of riding, which are contained in the guidelines written down in your Handbook, are absolutely superfluous and therefore unnecessary. These precepts, which the FEI has up until now felt obliged to uphold, are already fully developed, tried and tested! They are already recognized worldwide as authoritative, and as fair to the horse. Based on centuries of experience, they offer a stable and secure foundation even for today's riding.

No changes may be made that constitute a burden to the well-being of the horse, either physically or mentally. If you accept riding in hyperflexion as a permissible training method, you legitimize aggressive riding. We protest that in the strongest possible terms!

As horse people, we expect the FEI to maintain unaltered their regulations, which have until now been valid, resting as they do upon the classical precepts of riding—for the good of the horses and the continued good repute of international equestrian sport.

This letter was written by dressage Olympian Klaus Balkenhol and signed by many classically trained riders from different disciplines and different nations around the world.

In Appreciation

I have tried to present clearly, from the horse's point of view, what I have learned over many years of experience with students, clients, and horses. I've tried to share what I try to teach and how I have tried to live. I hope that my ideas regarding the relationship between mind and body, both in rider and in horse, can provide many people, even professional trainers, with a new perspective.

I give my thanks to all the two- and four-leggeds who have helped me to discover and study this perspective. It has encouraged me to be more critical of myself. In hindsight, not everything I have done in my riding career has been exactly right for the horse, as I would have preferred. Nevertheless, none of the horses with whom I formed a short or long partnership ever let me down. I am especially thankful to my best four-legged teachers, the so-called "difficult ones," "untalented ones," or the "ruined ones." They have shown me that classical training that respects the essence and personality of every single horse leads to success. These horses, who helped me more than I helped them, have all given me, after initial difficulties, that wonderful feeling that is a dialogue in motion. Sometimes sooner, sometimes later, they have all given me the feeling of dancing with a partner.

These experiences, and my study of "the classic" texts of equestrian literature with the perspective of today's mind-body science, have strengthened in me the conviction that the classical training method correctly applied is right for horse and rider. It is not necessary to "further develop" it since there is no more that you need to correctly train a horse. It is carefully designed to help the horse feel joy in being ridden, and holds as true for those horses not blessed by nature as for those born with the ability for harmonious, powerful, and truly beautiful movement.

Ulrike Thiel between her horses at the HippoCampus Institute for Equitherapy and Equine Sport Psychology in The Netherlands.

References

Joep und Tineke Bartels: **Bewuster Paardrijden** – de Trainingsmethoden van Academy Bartels, Forte Uitgevers 2006

Borstel, U.: **Fear in Horses and how it is affected by the rider, Trainingg and genetics.** Dissertation University of Guelph, Canada 2007

Gerd Heuschmann: **Finger in der Wunde;** Was Reiter wissen müssen, damit ihr Pferd gesund bleibt, Wu Wei 2008

Slijper, E.J.: **Comparative biologic-anatomical investigations on the vertebral column and spiral musculature of mammals.** IN Verh. Kon. Ned. Acad. v. Wetenschch. Afd. Nat.Kde., 2 Sect.D42, 1946

Eric von Breda: **A nonnatural head-neck position (Rollkur) during training results in less acute stress in elite, trained dressage horses.** In: Journ. Of Applied Animal Welfare Science 9/1/2006

Van Weeren: **Structure and biomechanical concept of the equine back;** Pferdeheilkunde 4/2004

Index